C000055813

more

NUMBER SKILLS

more NUMBER SKILLS

For National Curriculum levels 2-5

SPECTRUM MATHS

Dave Kirkby

Collins Educational

© Dave Kirkby 1993
ISBN 0 00 312550 5

Published by Collins Educational
77-85 Fulham Palace Road
Hammersmith, London W6 8JB

The purchase of this copyright material confers the right on the purchasing institution to photocopy the pupils' pages and special paper pages without any specific authorisation by the publisher. No other part of this publication may be reproduced, stored in a retrieval system, or transmitted in any form or by any means, electronic, mechanical, photocopying, recording or otherwise, without the prior permission of Collins Educational.

Illustrated by
Teri Gower

Designed by
Shireen Nathoo Design

Cover photographs of children by
Olly Hatch

Acknowledgement
We should like to thank NES Arnold Ltd, Nottingham, for kindly lending us the pictures of educational equipment for the cover.

Printed in Great Britain by
Martin's The Printers Ltd
Berwick upon Tweed

THE SPECTRUM MATHS SERIES

Starting	More	Go Further With
Investigations	Investigations	Investigations
Games	Games	Games
Data Handling	Data Handling	Data Handling
Algebra/Shape and Space	Algebra/Shape and Space	Algebra/Shape and Space
Number Skills	Number Skills	Number Skills

CONTENTS

1   Find The T

2   Pairs See-Saw

3   Subtracting With 6

4   Purses

5   Multiplication Tables

6   Consecutive Trains

7   What's Missing?

8   Fraction Shades

9   Triangle Corners

10 Dartboards

11 Temperature Scales

12 Table Numbers

13 Arrow Grids

14 Bean Bags

15 Dice Lines

16 Factor Pairs

17 Number Ties

18 2 X 2 Addition Squares

19 Twenties

20 Equation Solving

21 Multiplication Wheels

22 Nearly 60

23 Three From Four

24 Triangle Sums

25 Addition Grids

26 Cloud Numbers

27 Nearest 100

28 Arch Numbers

29 Nearest 10

30 Octagon Puzzle

31 Target Practice

32 Equation Puzzles

33 The Right Boxes

34 Magic Windmills

35 Magic Triangles

36 Differences

37 Addition Pyramids

38 Side Totals

39 Grid Pairs

40 Which Truck?

INTRODUCTION

Most schools use a mathematics scheme and teachers using these require a range of support material to supplement the scheme. Such material is provided by **Spectrum Maths**.

SPECTRUM MATHS: NUMBER SKILLS

This is a series of three books of number activities primarily for Key Stages 1 and 2, though much of it is also appropriate for Key Stage 3.

The books are defined in terms of three levels. Broadly, these levels are :
Starting Number Skills (Years 1, 2 and 3)
More Number Skills (Years 3, 4 and 5)
Go Further With Number Skills (Years 5, 6 and 7).

Each book contains:
40 pupil activities in the form of photocopymasters. There are also detailed teacher's notes accompanying each activity and Special Papers in the form of photocopymasters to help children record their work.

THE ACTIVITIES

A principal aim of mathematics teaching is to equip children to handle numbers with confidence. These activities provide an opportunity for children to practise number skills, with a strong emphasis on operational skills.

Each activity contains empty **number boxes** which children are required to complete, or sometimes colour. In most cases this is followed by an appropriate extension activity.

USING THE ACTIVITIES

The activities do not, in general, attempt to teach children the number skills they need. They provide practice and reinforcement for children who, having been introduced to the skills, need experiences to develop them.

Activities can be selected by the teacher to suit particular needs and situations. They can be used in a variety of ways:

► to integrate into the school mathematics programme
► to consolidate other work in the school mathematics scheme
► to provide enrichment material at appropriate times
► to form support material for responding to wide ranges of ability
► to complement other activities within the **Spectrum Maths** series.

In particular, many activities in the **Spectrum Games** and **Spectrum Investigations** series can be used in conjunction with this series to provide rich and varied opportunities for children to develop their skills.

THE TEACHER'S NOTES

The teacher's notes contain for each activity:

► clear indications of the content area
► details of any necessary apparatus
► notes outlining suggestions for introducing the activities
► ideas for extending the activities
► answers to the activities
► clearly identifiable National Curriculum references on a grid
► reference to related activities within the book and other books in the **Spectrum Maths** series.

USING THE TEACHER'S NOTES

LEVEL	UA	N	A	S	D
1					
2					
3					
4					
5					
6					
7					
8					
9					
10					

KEY
UA: Using and Applying Mathematics
N: Number
A: Algebra
S: Shape and Space
D: Handling Data

This section contains the answers to the activity. These appear as a reduced copy of the pupil activity sheet.

The table on the left refers to the Attainment Targets and Levels of the National Curriculum. An attempt has been made to locate, by means of dots in the table, the approximate content level for each activity, but it must be appreciated that many activities can be performed at a variety of different levels.

SKILLS

This section summarises the main content area of the activity.

APPARATUS

Details of necessary apparatus or special paper photocopymasters which are included at the back of the book

NOTE

This section contains suggestions for introducing the activity.

EXTENSION

This contains ideas for extending the activity.

SPECTRUM LINKS

	Data Handling	Games	Investigations	Algebra / S&S	Number Skills
Starting					
More		This section references related activities available throughout the Spectrum Series. The reference gives the number and title of the activity.			
Go Further With					

Find The T

LEVEL	UA	N	A	S	D
1					
2		●			
3			●		
4					
5					
6					
7					
8					
9					
10					

N2: Ordering numbers to at least 100
A3: Explaining number patterns and predicting subsequent numbers

SKILLS

► Recognising and extending patterns
► Ordering numbers from 1 to 36

NOTE

Before you begin this activity, illustrate and discuss various ways in which the numbers 1 to 36 can be ordered on a 6 x 6 grid. For example: horizontal patterns, vertical patterns, snake patterns, spiral patterns.

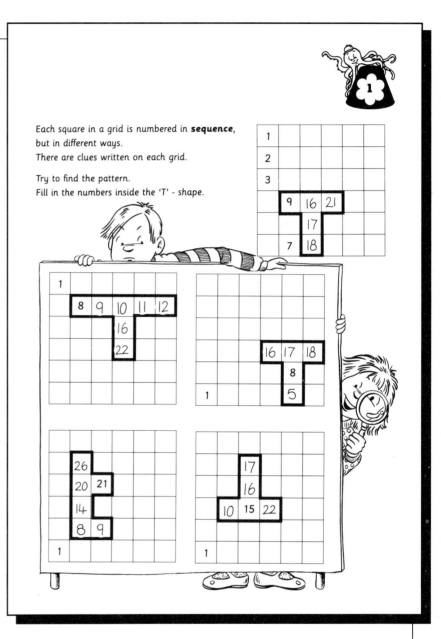

Each square in a grid is numbered in **sequence**, but in different ways.
There are clues written on each grid.

Try to find the pattern.
Fill in the numbers inside the 'T' - shape.

SPECTRUM LINKS

	Data Handling	Games	Investigations	Algebra/S&S	Number Skills
More			6 Table Patterns	7 Table Jigsaw 19 Unit Digit Patterns 20 Blobs	
Go Further With				9 Spirals	

Find the T

Each square in a grid is numbered in **sequence**, but in different ways.
There are clues written on each grid.

Try to find the pattern.
Fill in the numbers inside the 'T' - shape.

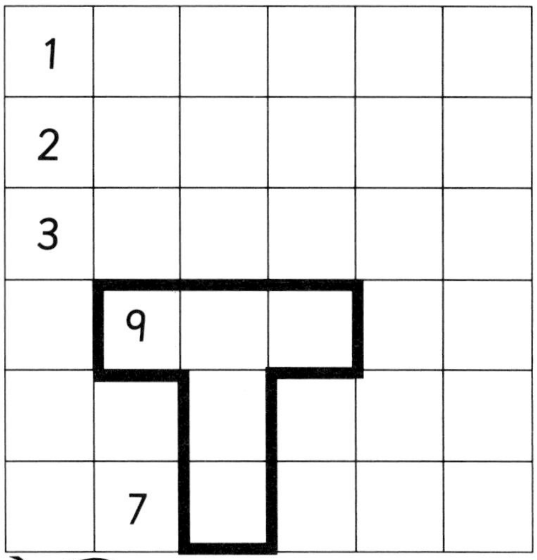

This page may be copied (see page 2) © Collins Educational 1992.

Pairs See-Saw

LEVEL	UA	N	A	S	D
1					
2	●	●	●		
3	●				
4	●				
5					
6					
7					
8					
9					
10					

N2: Learning and using addition and subtraction facts

A2: Exploring and using patterns in addition and subtraction facts to 10

SKILLS

► Adding several single-digit numbers

APPARATUS

Numbered cards, 1-9

NOTES

This is a good introduction to equations. Children can start by making a large drawing of the see-saw, so that the blocks can accommodate numbered cards. This can then be used to experiment with different arrangements.

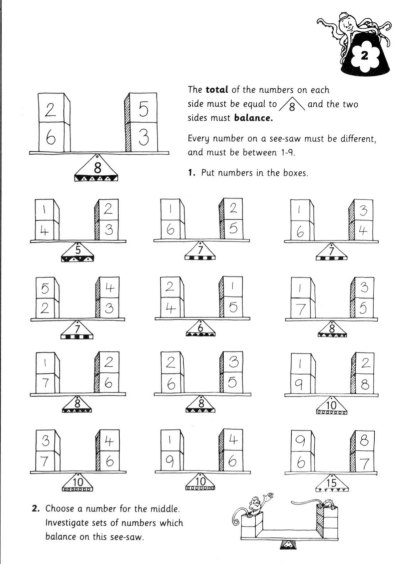

The **total** of the numbers on each side must be equal to ⟋8⟍ and the two sides must **balance**.

Every number on a see-saw must be different, and must be between 1-9.

1. Put numbers in the boxes.

2. Choose a number for the middle. Investigate sets of numbers which balance on this see-saw.

SPECTRUM LINKS

	Data Handling	Games	Investigations	Algebra/S&S	Number Skills
Starting			12 Keep Your Balance		30 3-Number See-Saws 37 4-Number See-Saws
Go Further With					10 Double See-Saws

Pairs See-Saw

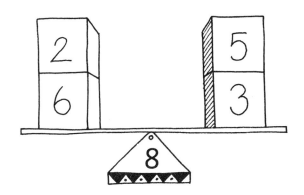

The **total** of the numbers on each side must be equal to △8 and the two sides must **balance.**

Every number on a see-saw must be different, and must be between 1-9.

1. Put numbers in the boxes.

2. Choose a number for the middle. Investigate sets of numbers which balance on this see-saw.

This page may be copied (see page 2) © Collins Educational 1992.

Subtracting With 6

LEVEL	UA	N	A	S	D
1					
2	●	●	●		
3	●				
4	●				
5					
6					
7					
8					
9					
10					

N2: Knowing and using addition and subtraction facts up to 10

A2: Exploring and using patterns in addition and subtraction facts to 10

SKILLS

► Subtracting single-digit numbers

APPARATUS

Numbered cards

NOTES

Children can draw a large picture of the subtractions, and experiment with the numbered cards placed in the boxes. Discuss systematic approaches. For example: fix a 6 at the top and explore all possibilities in the other two spaces. Then fix the 5, and so on.

1. Can you find 13 **different subtractions**, all with at least one 6 in them?
You can use any of the numbers from 0 to 9.
Two have been done for you.

$$\boxed{6} - \boxed{1} = \boxed{5}$$
$$\boxed{6} - \boxed{0} = \boxed{6}$$
$$\boxed{6} - \boxed{2} = \boxed{4}$$
$$\boxed{6} - \boxed{3} = \boxed{3}$$
$$\boxed{6} - \boxed{4} = \boxed{2}$$

$$\boxed{6} - \boxed{5} = \boxed{1}$$
$$\boxed{6} - \boxed{6} = \boxed{0}$$
$$\boxed{7} - \boxed{6} = \boxed{1}$$
$$\boxed{8} - \boxed{6} = \boxed{2}$$
$$\boxed{9} - \boxed{6} = \boxed{3}$$

$$\boxed{7} - \boxed{1} = \boxed{6}$$
$$\boxed{8} - \boxed{2} = \boxed{6}$$
$$\boxed{9} - \boxed{3} = \boxed{6}$$

2. Now see how many subtractions you can make with a 4 in each one.

SPECTRUM LINKS

	Data Handling	Games	Investigations	Algebra/S&S	Number Skills
Starting			**14** Card Tricks **29** Let's Add **39** Spot the Difference	**10** Stroking Cats **13** Spot Take Away **15** Hunt the Numbers **20** Subtraction Patterns	**9** Dice Totals **17** Adding **24** Card Game
More		**6** Six Sums	**17** Pairs with Patterns	**5** Taking Machines	

Subtracting with 6

1. Can you find 13 **different subtractions**, all with at least one 6 in them?
You can use any of the numbers from 0 to 9.
Two have been done for you.

```
  6        6        □        □        □
-  1     -  0     -  □     -  □     -  □
━━━━     ━━━━     ━━━━     ━━━━     ━━━━
  5        6        □        □        □


  □        □        □        □        □
-  □     -  □     -  □     -  □     -  □
━━━━     ━━━━     ━━━━     ━━━━     ━━━━
  □        □        □        □        □


  □        □        □
-  □     -  □     -  □
━━━━     ━━━━     ━━━━
  □        □        □
```

2. Now see how many subtractions you can make with a 4 in each one.

This page may be copied (see page 2) © Collins Educational 1992.

SPECTRUM MATHS ▲ MORE NUMBER SKILLS

Purses

LEVEL	UA	N	A	S	D
1					
2	●	●			
3	●				
4	●				
5					
6					
7					
8					
9					
10					

N2: Solving whole-number problems involving addition and subtraction including money

SKILLS

► Adding sums of money based on 5p, 10p and 20p coins
► Finding different ways of making a given sum of money

APPARATUS

Plastic coins

NOTE

Children can use plastic coins to explore how many different ways there are to make each of the various totals.

EXTENSION

► Carry out similar investigations with a change of coins, for example: 1p, 2p, 5p, 10p.

Which coins do you need to fill each purse?

1. In each line, colour enough coins to get **the right money** into the purse. Each line must be different. The first one has been done for you.

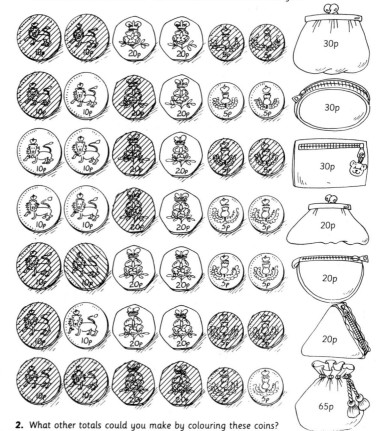

2. What other totals could you make by colouring these coins?

Question 2: the different totals possible are: 5p, 10p, 15p, 20p, 25p, 30p, 35p, 40p, 45p, 50p, 55p, 60p, 65p, 70p.

SPECTRUM LINKS

	Data Handling	Games	Investigations	Algebra/S&S	Number Skills
Starting		30 Banko 31 Change	7 Coin Count 15 Pick of the Pence 19 Three Coins		13 Coin Tables 18 Buying Presents 19 Choosing Coins

Purses

Which coins do you need to fill each purse?

1. In each line, colour enough coins to get **the right money** into the purse.
   Each line must be different. The first one has been done for you.

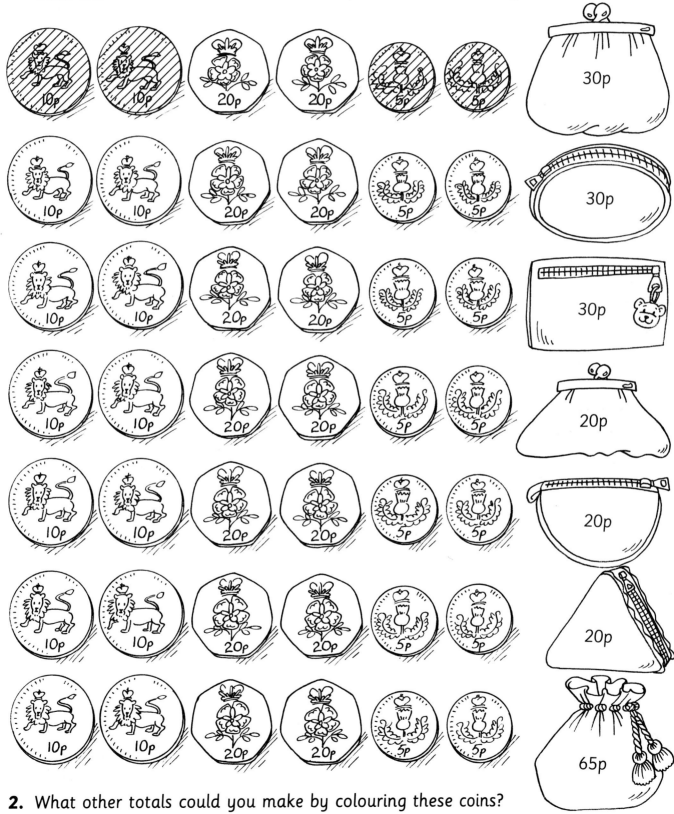

2. What other totals could you make by colouring these coins?

This page may be copied (see page 2) © Collins Educational 1992.

Multiplication Tables

LEVEL	UA	N	A	S	D
1					
2					
3					
4		●			
5					
6					
7					
8					
9					
10					

N4: Learning multiplication facts up to 10 x 10 and using them in multiplication and division problems

SKILLS

► Multiplying and dividing two numbers up to 10 x 10

APPARATUS

Playing cards (for the suggested extension)

EXTENSION

► Ask children to create their own 5 x 5 grid. The random arrangement of numbers to be multiplied can be found by shuffling a pack of cards (picture cards removed) and dealing out the numbers, five for the top and five for the side.

Fill in the gaps in these **multiplication tables**.

1.

X	2	3	4	5	6
2	4	6	8	10	12
3	6	9	12	15	18
4	8	12	16	20	24
5	10	15	20	25	30
6	12	18	24	30	36

X	9	7	10	6	8
3	27	21	30	18	24
7	63	49	70	42	56
5	45	35	50	30	40
4	36	28	40	24	32
6	54	42	60	36	48

2.

X	4	2	5	3	6
5	20	10	25	15	30
3	12	6	15	9	18
6	24	12	30	18	36
2	8	4	10	6	12
4	16	8	20	12	24

X	3	4	7	5	6
5	15	20	35	25	30
2	6	8	14	10	12
4	12	16	28	20	24
6	18	24	42	30	36
3	9	12	21	15	18

3.

X	7	8	9
7	49	56	63
8	56	64	72
9	63	72	81
10	70	80	90

X	5	6	7
3	15	18	21
4	20	24	28
5	25	30	35
6	30	36	42

SPECTRUM LINKS

	Data Handling	Games	Investigations	Algebra/S&S	Number Skills
Starting	28 Tables				
More		37 Snake Bite 38 Divido	6 Table Patterns 8 Table Ends	4 Doubling Up 7 Table Jigsaw 8 Completing Rectangles	12 Table Numbers 21 Multiplication Wheels
Go Further With	26 Sevens 36 Multiplication Tables	13 Race Track 20 Factor 24 Multiple Choice	9 Factors 13 Tables	4 Prime Numbers 17 Factor Graph	

Multiplication Tables

5

Fill in the gaps in these **multiplication tables**.

1.

X	2	3	4	5	6
2					
3		9			
4				20	
5					
6	12				

X	9	7	10	6	8
3					
7					
5					
4					
6					

2.

X	4	2	5	3	6
5	20			15	
3					
6			30		
2		4			
4				12	

X	3		7		6
5					
			14		
4		16			
					36
3				15	

3.

X			9
	49		
		72	
9	72		
	80		

X			
		21	
4	20	24	
	25		
		42	

This page may be copied (see page 2) © Collins Educational 1992.

Consecutive Trains

LEVEL	UA	N	A	S	D
1					
2	●				
3	●	●	●		
4	●	●			
5					
6					
7					
8					
9					
10					

N3: Learning and using addition and subtraction facts to 20

N4: Adding mentally several single-digit numbers. Adding mentally two two-digit numbers

A3: Explaining number patterns and predicting subsequent numbers

SKILLS

► Adding several single-digit numbers
► Selecting sets of consecutive numbers to make a given total

NOTE

It is possible to make consecutive trains for all engine numbers, except 1, 2, 4, 8, 16, 32, and so on.

EXTENSION

Discuss with children which engine numbers can be made with two trucks, with three trucks, and so on.

These are **consecutive trains**.
The numbers on the trucks must add up to the number on the engine.
They must also be **consecutive**. That means they must be in order and follow on directly from one another.

Here are two examples.

1. Look at the numbers on the engines below and then fill in the numbers on the trucks.

2. Draw some more trains, with different engine numbers, and trucks with consecutive numbers.

SPECTRUM LINKS

	Data Handling	Games	Investigations	Algebra/S&S	Number Skills
Starting					**2** Lucky Number Sweets
More			**21** Three in a Row		
Go Further With				**2** Puzzle Hotel	**29** Consecutive Flowers

Consecutive Trains

These are **consecutive trains**.

The numbers on the trucks must add up to the number on the engine.

They must also be **consecutive**. That means they must be in order and follow on directly from one another.

Here are two examples.

18 | 3 | 4 | 5 | 6

13 | 6 | 7

1. Look at the numbers on the engines below and then fill in the numbers on the trucks.

2. Draw some more trains, with different engine numbers, and trucks with consecutive numbers.

This page may be copied (see page 2) © Collins Educational 1992.

What's Missing?

LEVEL	UA	N	A	S	D
1					
2					●
3					
4		●			
5					
6					
7					
8					
9					
10					

N4: Adding and subtracting two two-digit numbers

D2: Collecting and recording data, leading to a frequency table

SKILLS

► Adding two two-digit numbers
► Finding missing digits in additions of two two-digit numbers

NOTE

Children can explore the most common missing digit by constructing a frequency table representing the use of each digit.

Digit	0 1 2 3 4 5 6 7 8 9
Frequency	

1. Find the **missing digits** in these sums.

$$\begin{array}{r} 2\ 3 \\ +1\ 4 \\ \hline 3\ \boxed{7} \end{array} \qquad \begin{array}{r} 3\ 2 \\ +4\ 5 \\ \hline \boxed{7}\ 7 \end{array} \qquad \begin{array}{r} 1\ 8 \\ +4\ \boxed{1} \\ \hline \boxed{5}\ 9 \end{array} \qquad \begin{array}{r} 2\ 3 \\ +\boxed{3}\ 6 \\ \hline 5\ \boxed{9} \end{array}$$

$$\begin{array}{r} 3\ 8 \\ +5\ 3 \\ \hline \boxed{9}\ \boxed{1} \end{array} \qquad \begin{array}{r} \boxed{4}\ 3 \\ +5\ 6 \\ \hline 9\ \boxed{9} \end{array} \qquad \begin{array}{r} 1\ \boxed{3} \\ +\boxed{7}\ 2 \\ \hline 8\ 5 \end{array} \qquad \begin{array}{r} 3\ 3 \\ +\boxed{3}\ 7 \\ \hline 7\ \boxed{0} \end{array}$$

$$\begin{array}{r} 2\ \boxed{7} \\ +\ \ 8\ 1 \\ \hline \boxed{1}\boxed{0}\ 8 \end{array} \qquad \begin{array}{r} 5\ \boxed{6} \\ +2\ 8 \\ \hline \boxed{8}\ 4 \end{array} \qquad \begin{array}{r} 4\ 2 \\ +1\ \boxed{9} \\ \hline \boxed{6}\ 1 \end{array} \qquad \begin{array}{r} \boxed{3}\ 7 \\ +1\ 8 \\ \hline 5\ \boxed{5} \end{array}$$

$$\begin{array}{r} 4\ 2 \\ +3\ 9 \\ \hline \boxed{8}\ \boxed{1} \end{array} \qquad \begin{array}{r} \boxed{1}\ 8 \\ +2\ \boxed{8} \\ \hline 4\ 6 \end{array} \qquad \begin{array}{r} 1\ \boxed{6} \\ +\boxed{4}\ 6 \\ \hline 6\ 2 \end{array} \qquad \begin{array}{r} 1\ 8 \\ +\boxed{3}\boxed{5} \\ \hline 5\ 3 \end{array}$$

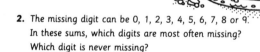

2. The missing digit can be 0, 1, 2, 3, 4, 5, 6, 7, 8 or 9. In these sums, which digits are most often missing? Which digit is never missing?

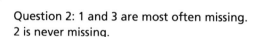

Question 2: 1 and 3 are most often missing.
2 is never missing.

SPECTRUM LINKS

	Data Handling	Games	Investigations	Algebra/S&S	Number Skills
Starting			**17** Totals		
More			**25** 4-Card Fun		**22** Nearly 60
Go Further With					**8** Nearly 20 **9** 5-Card Sums **17** Missing Subtractions

What's Missing?

1. Find the **missing digits** in these sums.

```
   2 3        3 2         1 8         2 3
 + 1 4      + 4 5       + 4 □       + □ 6
 ─────      ─────       ─────       ─────
   3 □        □ 7         □ 9         5 □
```

```
   3 8        □ 3         1 □         3 3
 + 5 3      + 5 6       + □ 2       + □ 7
 ─────      ─────       ─────       ─────
   □ □        9 □         8 5         7 □
```

```
   2 □        5 □         4 2         □ 7
 +   8 1    + 2 8       + 1 □       + 1 8
 ─────      ─────       ─────       ─────
  □ □ 8       □ 4         □ 1         5 □
```

```
   4 2        □ 8         1 □         1 8
 + 3 9      + 2 □       + □ 6       + □ □
 ─────      ─────       ─────       ─────
   □ □        4 6         6 2         5 3
```

2. The missing digit can be 0, 1, 2, 3, 4, 5, 6, 7, 8 or 9.
In these sums, which digits are most often missing?
Which digit is never missing?

This page may be copied (see page 2) © Collins Educational 1992.

Fraction Shades

LEVEL	UA	N	A	S	D
1					
2					
3					
4		●			
5					
6					
7					
8					
9					
10					

N4: Recognising and understanding simple fractions

SKILLS

► Recognising simple fractions
► Representing fractions by shading parts of different diagrams

EXTENSION

► The activity can be followed up by asking children to make their own 'fraction pictures' on squared paper.

1. Here are some circles with **fractions** shaded in.
Write down what fraction is **shaded** and what fraction has been left **unshaded**.
One has been done for you.

shaded	$\frac{1}{3}$
unshaded	$\frac{2}{3}$

shaded	$\frac{1}{2}$
unshaded	$\frac{1}{2}$

shaded	$\frac{1}{4}$
unshaded	$\frac{3}{4}$

shaded	$\frac{5}{6}$
unshaded	$\frac{1}{6}$

2. Shade these fraction pictures and complete the tables.

shaded	$\frac{3}{4}$
unshaded	$\frac{1}{4}$

shaded	$\frac{5}{8}$
unshaded	$\frac{3}{8}$

shaded	$\frac{1}{6}$
unshaded	$\frac{5}{6}$

shaded	$\frac{4}{9}$
unshaded	$\frac{5}{9}$

3. Colour or shade your own fractions on these pictures.
Write down what fraction is shaded and what fraction is unshaded.

shaded	
unshaded	

shaded	
unshaded	

shaded	
unshaded	

shaded	
unshaded	

SPECTRUM LINKS

	Data Handling	Games	Investigations	Algebra/S&S	Number Skills
Starting					**38** Colouring Fractions
More		**19** Fractions **28** Wheels		**14** Equivalent Fractions	
Go Further With					**30** Fraction Wheels **31** Fractions and Decimals **33** Tridiscs

Fraction Shades

8

1. Here are some circles with **fractions** shaded in.
Write down what fraction is **shaded** and what fraction has been left **unshaded**.
One has been done for you.

 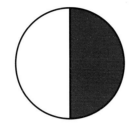 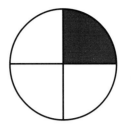 

shaded	$\frac{1}{3}$
unshaded	$\frac{2}{3}$

shaded	
unshaded	

shaded	
unshaded	

shaded	
unshaded	

2. Shade these fraction pictures and complete the tables.

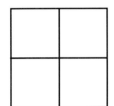 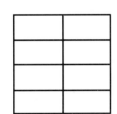 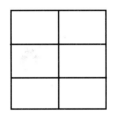 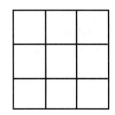

shaded	$\frac{3}{4}$
unshaded	

shaded	$\frac{5}{8}$
unshaded	

shaded	$\frac{1}{6}$
unshaded	

shaded	$\frac{4}{9}$
unshaded	

3. Colour or shade your own fractions on these pictures.
Write down what fraction is shaded and what fraction is unshaded.

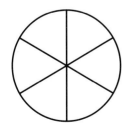 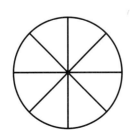 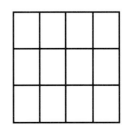 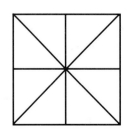

shaded	
unshaded	

shaded	
unshaded	

shaded	
unshaded	

shaded	
unshaded	

This page may be copied (see page 2) © Collins Educational 1992.

Triangle Corners

LEVEL	UA	N	A	S	D
1					
2	●				
3	●	●			
4	●	●			
5					
6					
7					
8					
9					
10					

N3: Learning and using addition and subtraction facts to 20

N4: Adding mentally several single-digit numbers

Estimating and approximating to check the validity of addition and subtraction calculations

SKILLS

► Adding three single-digit numbers
► Estimating the totals of several numbers
► Using a calculator to add several numbers

EXTENSION

► If it is known that the number inside a triangle is 10, for example, ask the children to explore how many different possible combinations of corner numbers there are.

The number inside each **triangle** is the **total** you reach when you add the numbers on each corner of the triangle.

1. Write the totals inside each triangle.

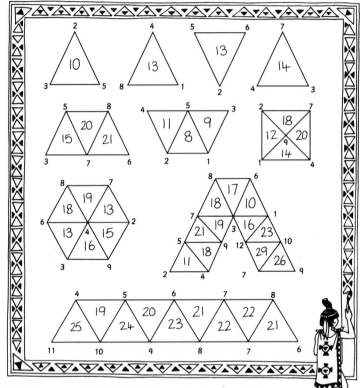

2. Make a guess at the total of all the numbers inside each shape. Use a calculator to see how close your guess is.

SPECTRUM LINKS

	Data Handling	Games	Investigations	Algebra/S&S	Number Skills
Starting			**23** Dice Sort		**20** Corner Numbers **31** Elephant Tricks
More		**1** Boxing **26** Fifteens	**2** Lucky 13 **11** Triplets		**10** Dartboards **14** Bean Bags **24** Triangle Sums

Triangle Corners

The number inside each **triangle** is the **total** you reach when you add the numbers on each corner of the triangle.

1. Write the totals inside each triangle.

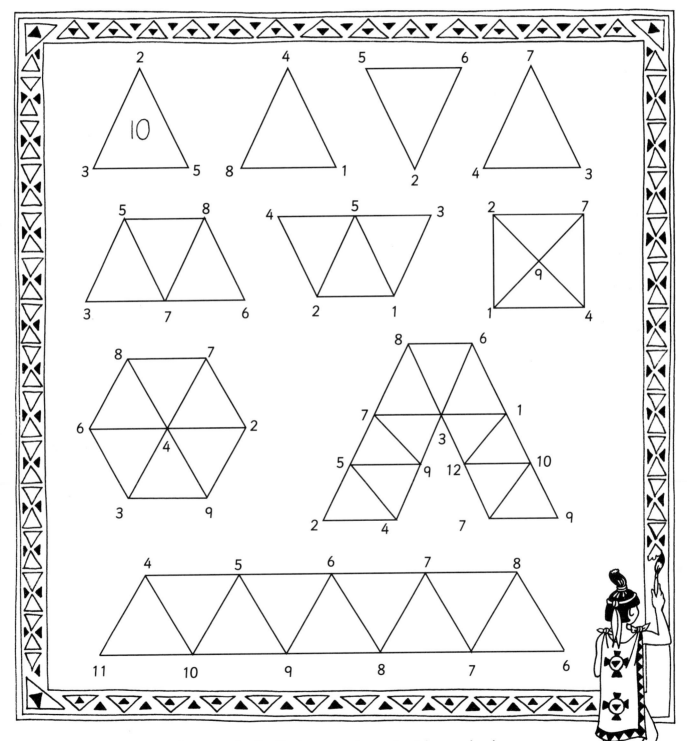

2. Make a guess at the total of all the numbers inside each shape.
Use a calculator to see how close your guess is.

Dartboards

LEVEL	UA	N	A	S	D
1					
2	●				
3	●	●			
4	●	●			
5					
6					
7					
8					
9					
10					

N3: Learning and using addition facts to 20
N4: Adding three single-digit numbers

SKILLS
► Doubling numbers up to 12
► Adding three numbers
► Finding different combinations of three numbers to add up to a given total

EXTENSION
► Children could go on to create their own dartboard puzzles.

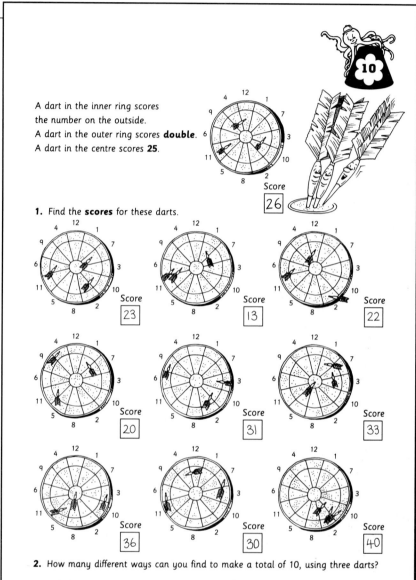

A dart in the inner ring scores the number on the outside.
A dart in the outer ring scores **double**.
A dart in the centre scores **25**.

Score 26

1. Find the **scores** for these darts.

Score 23 Score 13 Score 22
Score 20 Score 31 Score 33
Score 36 Score 30 Score 40

2. How many different ways can you find to make a total of 10, using three darts?

A total of 10 can be made using these darts in these ways:
Without doubles:
1,1,8 1,2,7 1,3,6 1,4,5 2,2,6 2,3,5 2,4,4 3,3,4
With doubles:
1,1,D4 1,D1,7 1,3,D3 1,D2,5 2,2,D3 2,D1,D3 D1,3,5
2,D2,4 2,D2,D2 D1,D2,D2 3,3,D2

SPECTRUM LINKS

	Data Handling	Games	Investigations	Algebra/S&S	Number Skills
Starting			23 Dice Sort		20 Corner Numbers 31 Elephant Tricks
More		1 Boxing 25 Darting 26 Fifteens	2 Lucky 13 11 Triplets		14 Bean Bags 24 Triangle Sums

Dartboards

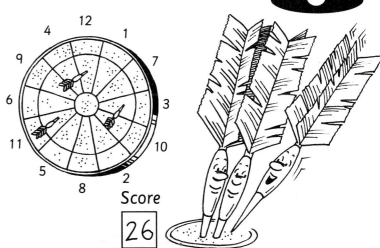

A dart in the inner ring scores
the number on the outside.
A dart in the outer ring scores **double**.
A dart in the centre scores **25**.

Score

26

1. Find the **scores** for these darts.

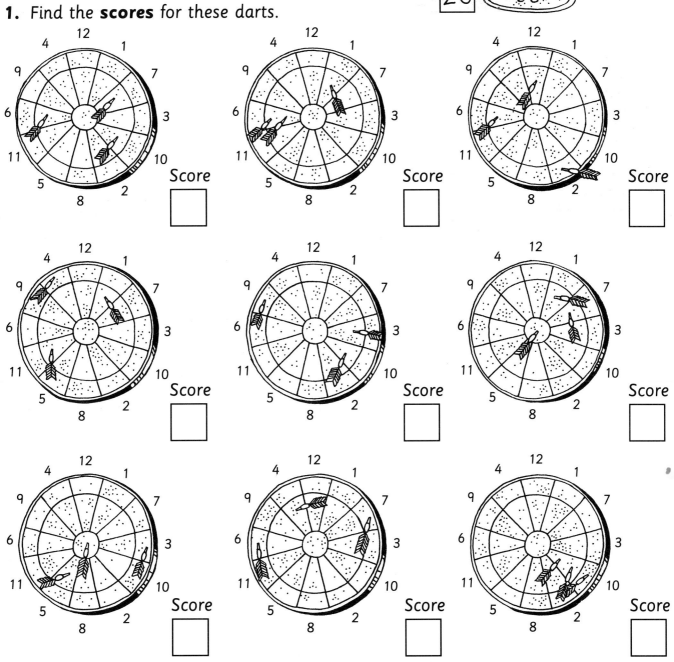

Score

Score

Score

Score

Score

Score

Score

Score

Score

2. How many different ways can you find to make a total of 10, using three darts?

This page may be copied (see page 2) © Collins Educational 1992.

Temperature Scales

11

LEVEL	UA	N	A	S	D
1					
2	●	●			
3	●	●			
4	●				
5					
6					
7					
8					
9					
10					

N2: Ordering numbers to at least 100
N3: Recognising negative whole numbers in familiar contexts
Interpreting numbers on a range of measuring instruments

SKILLS

► Reading a linear scale
► Locating points on a scale

APPARATUS

A daily newspaper

EXTENSION

► Children can monitor, daily, the temperature in different places over a period of several weeks. These can be recorded on a large graph showing how the temperature varies and changes in different parts of the world.

If you look in the newspaper, you can find out what the **temperature** has been, in different parts of the world.

1. The thermometer on the left shows you what the temperature was in all these places on 7 February, 1992. Write the temperature in the boxes.

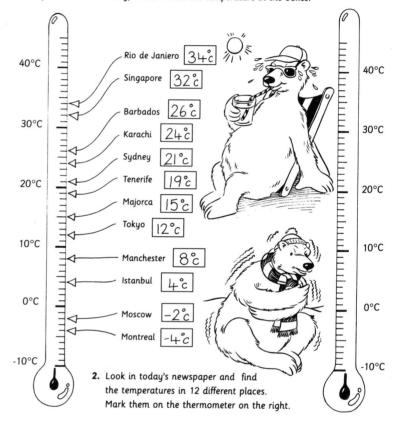

Rio de Janiero	34°c
Singapore	32°c
Barbados	26°c
Karachi	24°c
Sydney	21°c
Tenerife	19°c
Majorca	15°c
Tokyo	12°c
Manchester	8°c
Istanbul	4°c
Moscow	-2°c
Montreal	-4°c

2. Look in today's newspaper and find the temperatures in 12 different places. Mark them on the thermometer on the right.

SPECTRUM LINKS

	Data Handling	Games	Investigations	Algebra/S&S	Number Skills
Starting					27 Number Lines
More					**27** Nearest 100 **29** Nearest 10
Go Further With	**10** Around the World				

Temperature Scales

If you look in the newspaper, you can find out what the **temperature** has been, in different parts of the world.

1. The thermometer on the left shows you what the temperature was in all these places on 7 February, 1992. Write the temperature in the boxes.

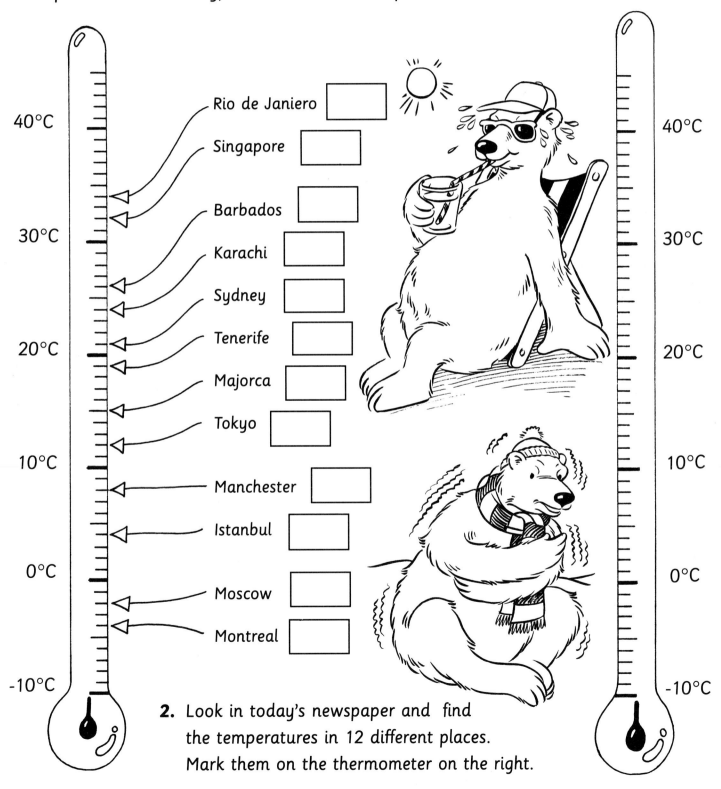

2. Look in today's newspaper and find the temperatures in 12 different places. Mark them on the thermometer on the right.

Table Numbers

LEVEL	UA	N	A	S	D
1					
2	●				
3	●				
4	●	●			
5					
6					
7					
8					
9					
10					

N4: Learning multiplication facts up to 10 x 10 and using them in multiplication and division problems

SKILLS

► Multiplying two numbers up to 10 x 10
► Using a calculator to add nine numbers
► Searching for numerical relationships

APPARATUS

Calculators

NOTE

Invite children to guess the totals of the table numbers before using the calculator.

Here is a **multiplication table**. Can you see how the numbers in the table were worked out?

x	1	3	6
1	1	3	6
3	3	9	18
6	6	18	36

1. Use a calculator to find the total of all the **table numbers**:

$$1 + 3 + 6 + 3 + 9 + 18 + 6 + 18 + 36 = \boxed{100}$$

2. Now complete these tables, then find the total of the **table numbers**.

x	1	4	5
1	1	4	5
4	4	16	20
5	5	20	25

Table number total $\boxed{100}$

x	5	3	2
5	25	15	10
3	15	9	6
2	10	6	4

Table number total $\boxed{100}$

x	2	1	7
3	6	3	21
6	12	6	42
1	2	1	7

Table number total $\boxed{100}$

x	3	4	3
4	12	16	12
1	3	4	3
5	15	20	15

Table number total $\boxed{100}$

3. What do you notice about the totals of the table numbers?

4. Can you invent some more multiplication tables with these totals?

5. Can you invent some multiplication tables with table numbers to total 144?

Questions 3 and 5: the totals are 100, because each row heading and each column heading has a total of 10. The table number total is the result of multiplying 10 by 10 in stages.

If the table number total is 144, then the row and column headings must each total 12.

SPECTRUM LINKS

	Data Handling	Games	Investigations	Algebra/S&S	Number Skills
Starting	28 Tables				
More		37 Snake Bite 38 Divido	6 Table Patterns 8 Table Ends	4 Doubling Up 7 Table Jigsaw 8 Completing Rectangles	5 Multiplication Tables 21 Multiplication Wheels
Go Further With	26 Sevens 36 Multiplication Tables	13 Race Track 20 Factor	9 Factors 13 Tables	4 Prime Numbers 17 Factor Graph	

Table Numbers

Here is a **multiplication table**.
Can you see how the numbers in
the table were worked out?

x	1	3	6
1	1	3	6
3	3	9	18
6	6	18	36

1. Use a calculator to find the
total of all the **table numbers**:

$$1 + 3 + 6 + 3 + 9 + 18 + 6 + 18 + 36 = \boxed{}$$

2. Now complete these tables, then find the total of the **table numbers**.

x	1	4	5
1			
4			
5			

Table number total [   ]

x	5	3	2
5			
3			
2			

Table number total [   ]

x	2	1	7
3			
6			
1			

Table number total [   ]

x	3	4	3
4			
1			
5			

Table number total [   ]

3. What do you notice about the totals of the table numbers?

4. Can you invent some more multiplication tables with these totals?

5. Can you invent some multiplication tables with table numbers to total 144?

Arrow Grids

LEVEL	UA	N	A	S	D
1					
2	●	●			
3	●	●			
4	●				
5					
6					
7					
8					
9					
10					

N2/3: Learning and using addition and subtraction facts

SKILLS

► Adding and subtracting constant numbers
► Searching for numerical relationships

EXTENSIONS

► Invite children to predict the numbers in the different squares in, for example, this arrow grid:

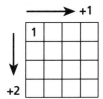

► Extend this work to other arrow grids which they can either devise for themselves, or which you make.

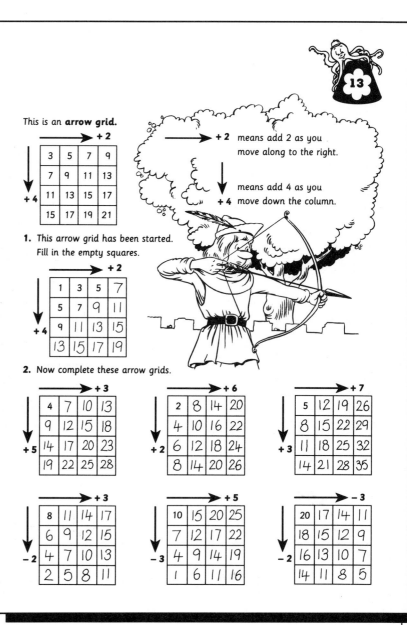

This is an **arrow grid**.

→ +2 means add 2 as you move along to the right.

↓ +4 means add 4 as you move down the column.

1. This arrow grid has been started. Fill in the empty squares.

2. Now complete these arrow grids.

SPECTRUM LINKS

	Data Handling	Games	Investigations	Algebra/S&S	Number Skills
Starting					**21** Grids
Go Further With					**16** Multiplying Grids

Arrow Grids

This is an **arrow grid.**

$\longrightarrow$ **+ 2**

3	5	7	9
7	9	11	13
11	13	15	17
15	17	19	21

↓ **+ 4**

$\longrightarrow$ **+ 2** means add 2 as you move along to the right.

↓ **+ 4** means add 4 as you move down the column.

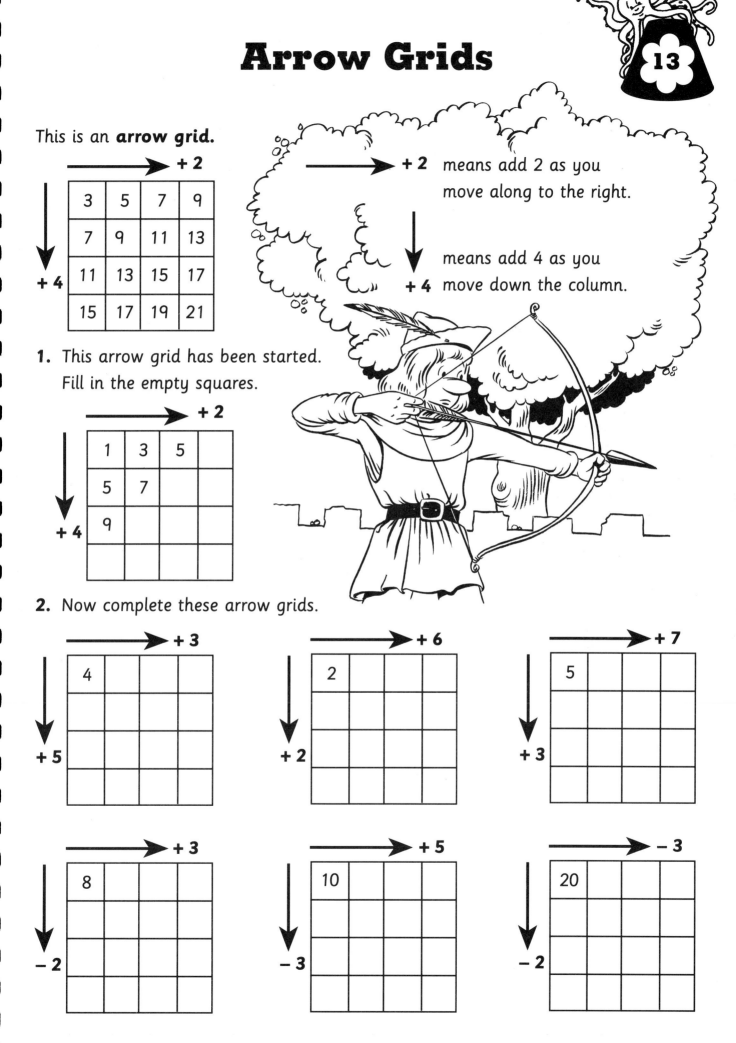

1. This arrow grid has been started. Fill in the empty squares.

$\longrightarrow$ **+ 2**

1	3	5	
5	7		
9			

↓ **+ 4**

2. Now complete these arrow grids.

$\longrightarrow$ **+ 3**

4			

↓ **+ 5**

$\longrightarrow$ **+ 6**

2			

↓ **+ 2**

$\longrightarrow$ **+ 7**

5			

↓ **+ 3**

$\longrightarrow$ **+ 3**

8			

↓ **– 2**

$\longrightarrow$ **+ 5**

10			

↓ **– 3**

$\longrightarrow$ **– 3**

20			

↓ **– 2**

This page may be copied (see page 2) © Collins Educational 1992.

SPECTRUM MATHS ▲ MORE NUMBER SKILLS

Bean Bags

LEVEL	UA	N	A	S	D
1					
2					
3		●			
4		●			
5					
6					
7					
8					
9					
10					

N3: Ordering numbers to at least 1000
N4: Adding two two-digit numbers

SKILLS

► Adding five multiples of 10
► Ordering two- and three- digit numbers

EXTENSIONS

► Children can follow up this activity by investigating how many different totals are possible as a result of five throws.
► Also, they could design their own bean bag game with different points, and explore some totals.

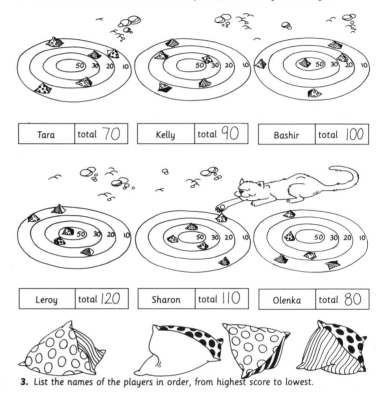

Some children are playing a game with **bean bags**.
They each have five bags to throw on to the target.
You can see how each child scores.

1. Guess who is the winner.

2. Now work out the total score for each person, and see if you were right.

| Tara | total 70 | | Kelly | total 90 | | Bashir | total 100 |

| Leroy | total 120 | | Sharon | total 110 | | Olenka | total 80 |

3. List the names of the players in order, from highest score to lowest.

The players should be listed in the following order: Leroy –120; Sharon – 110; Bashir –100; Kelly – 90; Olenka – 80; Tara – 70.

SPECTRUM LINKS

	Data Handling	Games	Investigations	Algebra/S&S	Number Skills
More					**10** Dartboards

Bean Bags

Some children are playing a game with **bean bags**.
They each have five bags to throw on to the target.
You can see how each child scores.

1. Guess who is the winner.

2. Now work out the total score for each person, and see if you were right.

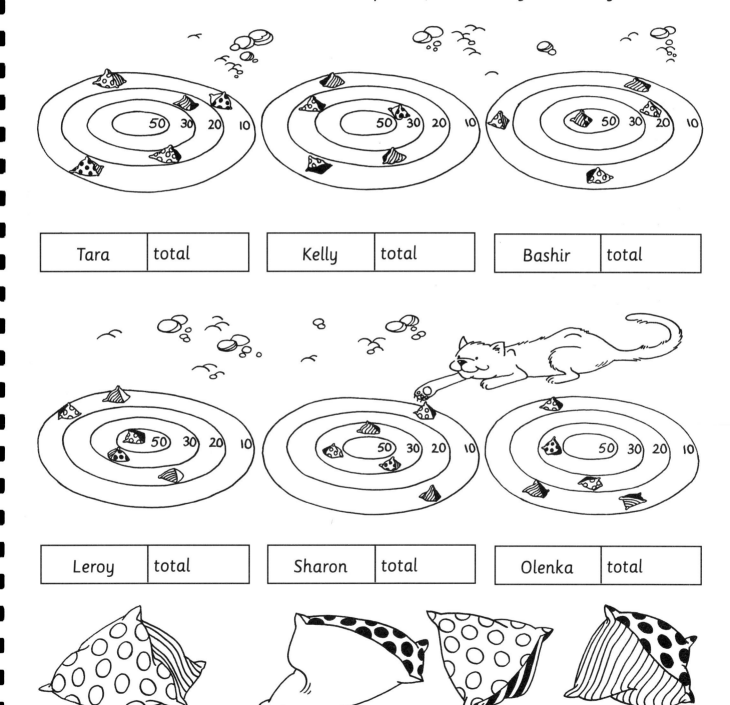

Tara	total

Kelly	total

Bashir	total

Leroy	total

Sharon	total

Olenka	total

3. List the names of the players in order, from highest score to lowest.

This page may be copied (see page 2) © Collins Educational 1992.

Dice Lines

LEVEL	UA	N	A	S	D
1					
2	●				
3	●	●			
4	●	●	●		
5					
6					
7					
8					
9					
10					

A3: Simple equations
N3/4: Addition, subtraction, multiplication and division

SKILLS
► Creating expressions for numbers using combinations of addition, subtraction, multiplication and division

APPARATUS
Three dice, 72 counters

EXTENSION
► Make a large grid and pin it to the wall, so that children can write expressions for each number in the box, with the number. Children can be challenged to find and write missing expressions, to complete the grid.

1	2	3	4	5	6	8	9
10	11	12	14	15	17	18	19
20	21	22	23	24	25	26	28
31	32	33	34	36	37	38	39
42	43	44	45	46	47	48	49
50	52	53	54	55	56	57	58
60	61	62	64	65	66	68	69
70	72	73	74	75	76	77	78

Suppose you throw three **dice** and get these numbers ➡

You can use the three digits 2, 5 and 6 (not more than once each time) to make **different** numbers on the grid.

So, for example, you can make 9 this way: 6 + 5 - 2.
You can make 17 this way: (2 x 6) + 5. You can make 31 this way: 26 + 5

1. Throw three dice.
   Use the dice numbers to make as many numbers from the grid as you can.
   Colour the numbers you make.
   Write down how you made each number on another piece of paper.

2. When you have coloured as many numbers as you can,
   throw the three dice again.
   This time use counters to cover up the numbers on the grid.

3. You could keep going, and see how many throws
   you must make to get a counter on every square.

SPECTRUM LINKS

	Data Handling	Games	Investigations	Algebra/S&S	Number Skills
Starting		13 Big Match 18 Summary 27 Choosy	10 Trios 12 Keep your Balance 14 Card Tricks	6 Shape Search 10 Stroking Cats 15 Hunt the Numbers	
More		3 Boxer 8 Dice Superstars	29 Asking Questions	10 Mystery People	20 Equation Solving 28 Arch Numbers 31 Target Practice
Go Further With		8 A Mouthful 33 Challenge 38 Switch	16 Number Nine 21 Equations 33 Signs	7 Number Tricks 10 Think of a Number 14 Whodunnit?	6 Countdown 7 Mixed Equations 13 Three Spots 15 A Special Date

Dice Lines

1	2	3	4	5	6	8	9
10	11	12	14	15	17	18	19
20	21	22	23	24	25	26	28
31	32	33	34	36	37	38	39
42	43	44	45	46	47	48	49
50	52	53	54	55	56	57	58
60	61	62	64	65	66	68	69
70	72	73	74	75	76	77	78

Suppose you throw three **dice**
and get these numbers ⟶

You can use the three digits 2, 5 and 6 (not more than once each time) to make
different numbers on the grid.

So, for example, you can make 9 this way: 6 + 5 - 2.
You can make 17 this way: (2 x 6) + 5. You can make 31 this way: 26 + 5

1. Throw three dice.
   Use the dice numbers to make as many numbers from the grid as you can.
   Colour the numbers you make.
   Write down how you made each number on another piece of paper.

2. When you have coloured as many numbers as you can,
   throw the three dice again.
   This time use counters to cover up the numbers on the grid.

3. You could keep going, and see how many throws
   you must make to get a counter on every square.

Factor Pairs

LEVEL	UA	N	A	S	D
1					
2	●				
3	●	●			
4	●	●	●		
5					
6					
7					
8					
9					
10					

N4:   Learning multiplication facts up to 10 x 10 and using them in multiplication and division problems

A4:   Generalising, mainly in words, patterns which arise in various situations, eg 'factor'

SKILLS

► Finding different pairs of factors for given numbers
► Multiplying two numbers together

EXTENSION

► Children can attempt to sort different plants according to their number of factor pairs. Discuss which plants have many factor pairs, and which have only one.

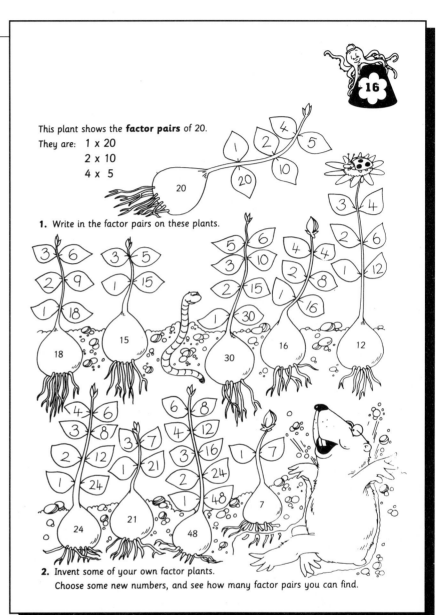

This plant shows the **factor pairs** of 20.
They are: 1 x 20
            2 x 10
            4 x 5

1. Write in the factor pairs on these plants.

2. Invent some of your own factor plants.
Choose some new numbers, and see how many factor pairs you can find.

SPECTRUM LINKS

	Data Handling	Games	Investigations	Algebra/S&S	Number Skills
More		**37** Snake Bite **38** Divido	**6** Table Patterns **7** Pick Your Cards **8** Table Ends	**8** Completing Rectangles **12** Sift the Multiples **13** Table Patterns	**26** Cloud Numbers
Go Further With	**36** Multiplication Tables	**13** Race Track **20** Factor **24** Multiple Choice	**9** Factors **13** Tables	**4** Prime Numbers **17** Factor Graph **18** Multiplication Machines	**11** Lowest Common Multiples **12** Factor Show **18** Factor Grids **25** Highest Common Factors

Factor Pairs

This plant shows the **factor pairs** of 20.

They are: 1 x 20
             2 x 10
             4 x 5

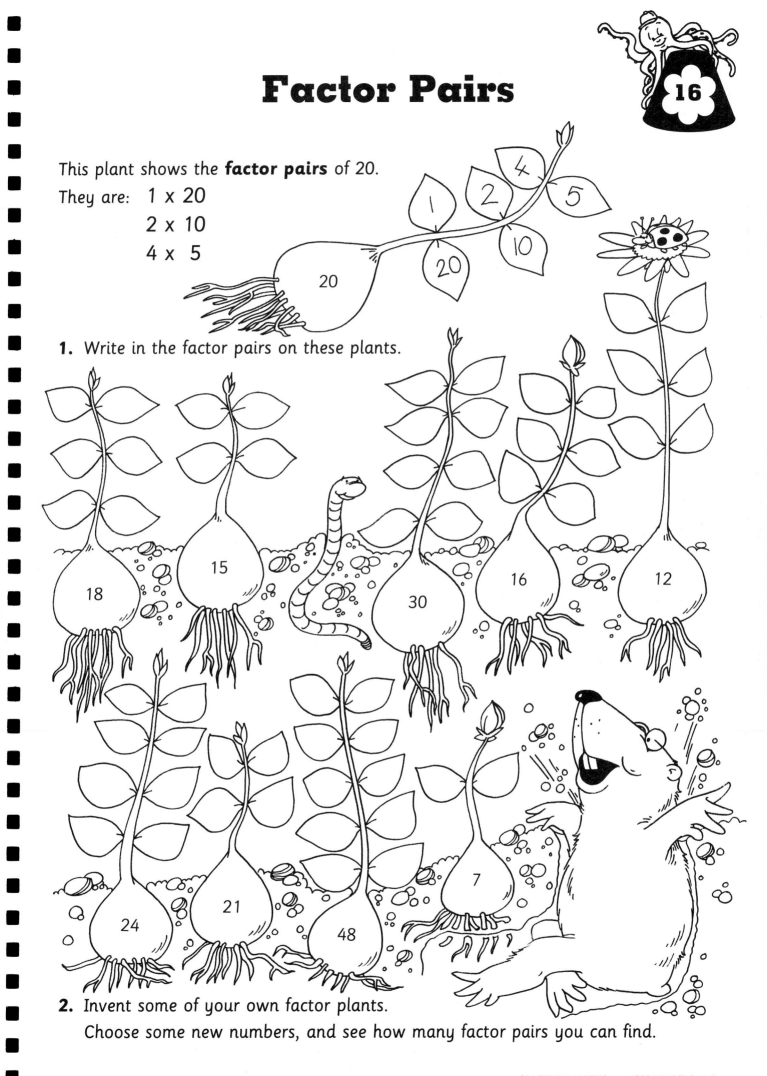

1. Write in the factor pairs on these plants.

18   15   30   16   12

24   21   48   7

2. Invent some of your own factor plants.
Choose some new numbers, and see how many factor pairs you can find.

Number Ties

LEVEL	UA	N	A	S	D
1					
2	●				
3	●	●			
4	●	●			
5					
6					
7					
8					
9					
10					

N3: Learning and using addition and multiplication facts to 20

N4: Learning multiplication facts up to 10 x 10 and using them in multiplication and division problems
Adding mentally several single-digit numbers

SKILLS

► Calculating the result of successions of number operations on given numbers

APPARATUS

Special Paper 1

EXTENSION

► Ask children to explore variations in a particular tie for different 'knot numbers'.

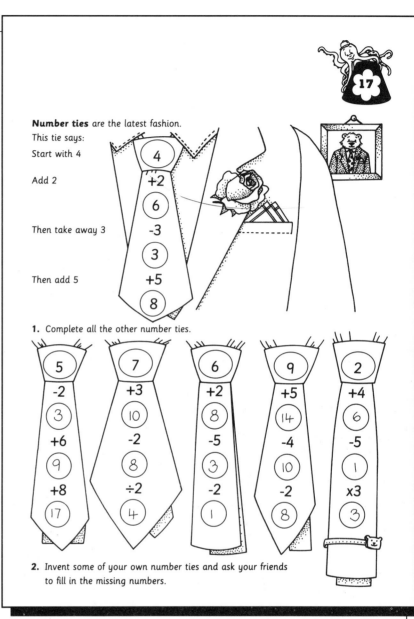

Number ties are the latest fashion.
This tie says:

Start with 4

Add 2

Then take away 3

Then add 5

4
+2
6
-3
3
+5
8

1. Complete all the other number ties.

5	7	6	9	2
-2	+3	+2	+5	+4
3	10	8	14	6
+6	-2	-5	-4	-5
9	8	3	10	1
+8	÷2	-2	-2	x3
17	4	1	8	3

2. Invent some of your own number ties and ask your friends to fill in the missing numbers.

SPECTRUM LINKS

	Data Handling	Games	Investigations	Algebra/S&S	Number Skills
Go further With				**7** Number Tricks **10** Think of a Number	

Number Ties

Number ties are the latest fashion.

This tie says:

Start with 4

Add 2

Then take away 3

Then add 5

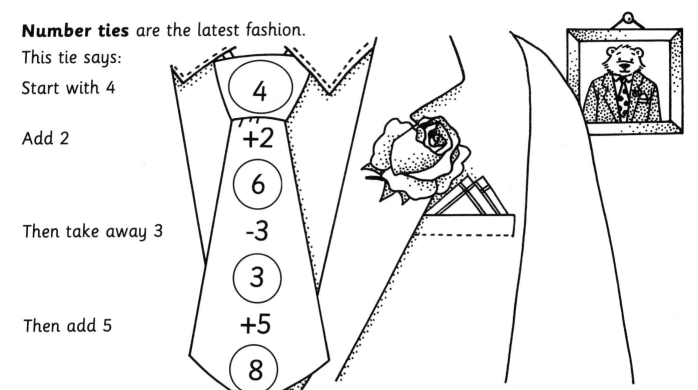

1. Complete all the other number ties.

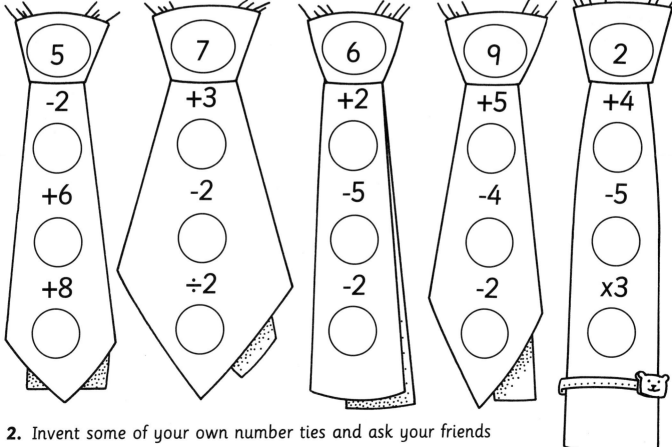

2. Invent some of your own number ties and ask your friends to fill in the missing numbers.

This page may be copied (see page 2) © Collins Educational 1992.

18 2 x 2 Addition Squares

LEVEL	UA	N	A	S	D
1					
2	●	●			
3	●	●			
4	●				
5					
6					
7					
8					
9					
10					

N2/3: Learning and using addition and subtraction facts

SKILLS

► Adding and subtracting

APPARATUS

Numbered cards, 1-9

NOTE

Arrange numbered cards on a 2 x 2 grid when solving the more difficult later puzzles.

EXTENSION

► The activity can be extended to using larger numbers.

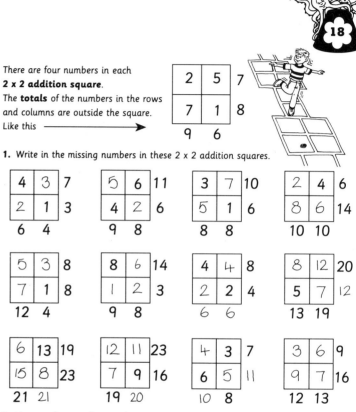

There are four numbers in each **2 x 2 addition square**.
The **totals** of the numbers in the rows and columns are outside the square.
Like this ──────────►

```
2 | 5  7
7 | 1  8
9   6
```

1. Write in the missing numbers in these 2 x 2 addition squares.

```
4 3 | 7      5 6 | 11     3 7 | 10     2 4 | 6
2 1 | 3      4 2 | 6      5 1 | 6      8 6 | 14
 6 4          9 8          8 8         10 10

5 3 | 8      8 6 | 14     4 4 | 8      8 12 | 20
7 1 | 8      1 2 | 3      2 2 | 4      5  7 | 12
12 4          9 8          6 6         13 19

6 13 | 19    12 11 | 23   4 3 | 7      3 6 | 9
15 8 | 23     7  9 | 16   6 5 | 11     9 7 | 16
21 21         19 20       10 8        12 13
```

2. Here are four puzzles to solve.
You may only use these as missing numbers: 4, 5, 6, 7, 8.

```
4 5 | 9      8 6 | 14     5 7 | 12     6 4 | 10
7 8 | 15     4 5 | 9      6 4 | 10     7 8 | 15
11 13        12 11        11 11       13 12
```

3. Invent four more puzzles using these as missing numbers: 2, 3, 5, 8, 9.

SPECTRUM LINKS

	Data Handling	Games	Investigations	Algebra/S&S	Number Skills
More					25 Addition Grids 26 Cloud Numbers
Go Further With			12 Times Square		

2 x 2 Addition Squares

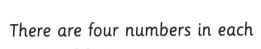

There are four numbers in each
2 x 2 addition square.
The **totals** of the numbers in the rows
and columns are outside the square.
Like this ——————➤

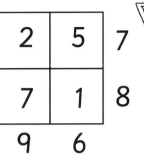

2	5	7
7	1	8
9	6	

1. Write in the missing numbers in these 2 x 2 addition squares.

4		7
	1	3
6	4	

	6	11
4		6
9	8	

3		10
	1	6
8	8	

	4	6
		14
10	10	

		8
	1	8
12	4	

8		14
		3
9	8	

4		8
	2	4

		20
5		
13	19	

	13	19
		23
21		

		23
	9	16
19		

	3	7
6		
	8	

		9
		16
12	13	

2. Here are four puzzles to solve.
You may only use these as missing numbers: 4, 5, 6, 7, 8.

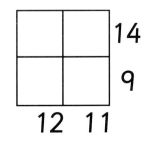

		9
		15
11	13	

		14
		9
12	11	

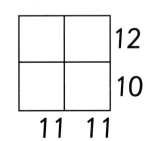

		12
		10
11	11	

		10
		15
13	12	

3. Invent four more puzzles using these as missing numbers: 2, 3, 5, 8, 9.

This page may be copied (see page 2) © Collins Educational 1992.

Twenties

LEVEL	UA	N	A	S	D
1					
2					
3					
4		●			
5					
6					
7					
8					
9					
10					

N4: Adding several single digit numbers

SKILLS

► Adding several single-digit numbers
► Searching for sets of numbers which have a given total

NOTES

Children could draw templates of the various shapes on tracing paper. If these are placed over the grid, they can be used to identify numbers in the right arrangement, which add up to 20.

EXTENSION

► Children can choose further numbers and look for shapes containing appropriate numbers.

Each of the shapes below shows part of the **number grid**.

1. Each shape contains numbers which add up to **20**.

   Can you find them?
   Write in the numbers.
   One has been done for you.

2	1	3	2	1
4	6	1	5	5
3	1	5	4	3
4	2	4	6	2
3	6	5	1	6

2. Now find shapes that add up to 15.

SPECTRUM LINKS

	Data Handling	Games	Investigations	Algebra/S&S	Number Skills
Starting			35 In the Window		4 Giraffe 12 Difference Dog 31 Elephant Tricks
More					39 Grid Pairs
Go Further With					23 Multiples of 10 26 Hexanimals

Twenties

Each of the shapes below shows part of the **number grid**.

1. Each shape contains numbers which add up to **20**.

   Can you find them?
   Write in the numbers.
   One has been done for you.

2	1	3	2	1
4	6	1	5	5
3	1	5	4	3
4	2	4	6	2
3	6	5	1	6

2. Now find shapes that add up to 15.

This page may be copied (see page 2) © Collins Educational 1992.

Equation Solving

LEVEL	UA	N	A	S	D
1					
2	●	●	●		
3	●	●			
4	●				
5					
6					
7					
8					
9					
10					

N2/3: Learning and using addition and subtraction facts

A2: Understanding the use of a symbol to stand for an unknown number

SKILLS

► Solving equations involving combinations of addition and subtraction

NOTE

The most difficult type of equation to create is:

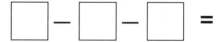

It is easiest when one of the numbers is relatively much larger than the others.

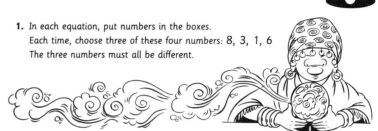

1. In each equation, put numbers in the boxes.
Each time, choose three of these four numbers: 8, 3, 1, 6
The three numbers must all be different.

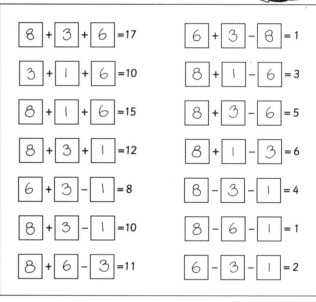

$$8 + 3 + 6 = 17 \qquad 6 + 3 - 8 = 1$$
$$3 + 1 + 6 = 10 \qquad 8 + 1 - 6 = 3$$
$$8 + 1 + 6 = 15 \qquad 8 + 3 - 6 = 5$$
$$8 + 3 + 1 = 12 \qquad 8 + 1 - 3 = 6$$
$$6 + 3 - 1 = 8 \qquad 8 - 3 - 1 = 4$$
$$8 + 3 - 1 = 10 \qquad 8 - 6 - 1 = 1$$
$$8 + 6 - 3 = 11 \qquad 6 - 3 - 1 = 2$$

2. Invent a set of equations for your friend to do.
Ask him or her to use any three of the numbers: 5, 4, 2, 6

3. Invent some equations using a set of four larger numbers.

SPECTRUM LINKS

	Data Handling	Games	Investigations	Algebra/S&S	Number Skills
Starting		13 Big Match 18 Summary 27 Choosy	10 Trios 12 Keep your Balance 14 Card Tricks	6 Shape Search 10 Stroking Cats 15 Hunt the Numbers	
More		3 Boxer 8 Dice Superstars	29 Asking Questions	10 Mystery People	15 Dice Lines 28 Arch Numbers 31 Target Practice
Go Further With		8 A Mouthful 33 Challenge 38 Switch	16 Number Nine 21 Equations 33 Signs	7 Number Tricks 10 Think of a Number 14 Whodunnit?	6 Countdown 7 Mixed Equations 3 Three Spots 15 A Special Date

Equation Solving

1. In each equation, put numbers in the boxes.
Each time, choose three of these four numbers: 8, 3, 1, 6
The three numbers must all be different.

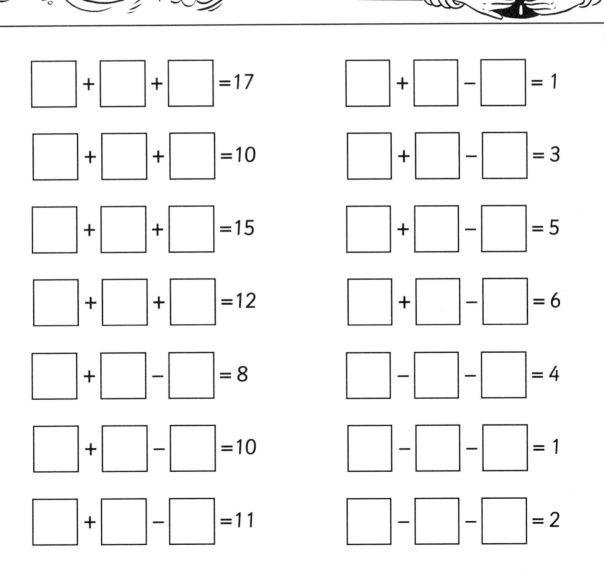

☐ + ☐ + ☐ = 17   ☐ + ☐ − ☐ = 1

☐ + ☐ + ☐ = 10   ☐ + ☐ − ☐ = 3

☐ + ☐ + ☐ = 15   ☐ + ☐ − ☐ = 5

☐ + ☐ + ☐ = 12   ☐ + ☐ − ☐ = 6

☐ + ☐ − ☐ = 8   ☐ − ☐ − ☐ = 4

☐ + ☐ − ☐ = 10   ☐ − ☐ − ☐ = 1

☐ + ☐ − ☐ = 11   ☐ − ☐ − ☐ = 2

2. Invent a set of equations for your friend to do.
Ask him or her to use any three of the numbers: 5, 4, 2, 6

3. Invent some equations using a set of four larger numbers.

This page may be copied (see page 2) © Collins Educational 1992.

Multiplication Wheels

LEVEL	UA	N	A	S	D
1					
2	●				
3	●				
4	●	●			
5					
6					
7					
8					
9					
10					

N4: Learning multiplication facts up to 10 x 10 and using them in multiplication and division problems
Multiplying and dividing two-digit numbers by a single-digit number

SKILLS

► Multiplying one single-digit number by another
► Division of a two-digit number by a single-digit number

APPARATUS

Special Paper 2

NOTE

Children can use Special Paper 2 to make their own multiplication wheels.

EXTENSION

► Try using wheel numbers greater than 10.

These **multiplication wheels** have three numbers on them, when they are complete.
There is the **rim number**, the **wheel number** and the **hub number**, which is right in the middle.

You can find the rim number by multiplying the hub number by the wheel number.

1. Fill in the gaps on the wheels. Two have been done for you.

2. Each rim number has a letter by it. Write these down according to the order of the numbers, starting with the lowest number.
   Which countries' names have you spelled?

PORTUGAL

SCOTLAND

BULGARIA

COLOMBIA

3. Build your own multiplication wheels with these hubs: x3, x7, x9, x10.

SPECTRUM LINKS

	Data Handling	Games	Investigations	Algebra/S&S	Number Skills
Starting	28 Tables				11 Addition Wheels
More		37 Snake Bite 38 Divido	6 Table Patterns 8 Table Ends	4 Doubling Up 7 Table Jigsaw 8 Completing Rectangles	12 Table Numbers
Go Further With	26 Sevens 36 Multiplication Tables	13 Race Track 20 Factor 24 Multiple Choice	9 Factors 13 Tables	4 Prime Numbers 17 Factor Graph	

Multiplication Wheels

These **multiplication wheels** have three numbers on them,
when they are complete.
There is the **rim number**, the **wheel number** and the **hub number**,
which is right in the middle.

You can find the rim number by multiplying the hub number by the wheel number.

1. Fill in the gaps on the wheels. Two have been done for you.

2. Each rim number has a letter by it. Write these down according to the order of
   the numbers, starting with the lowest number.
   Which countries' names have you spelled?

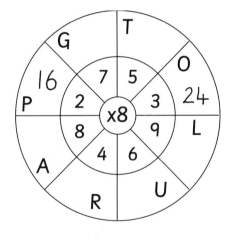

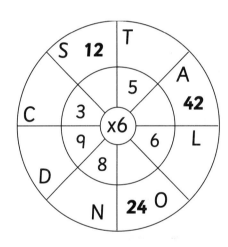

_ _ _ _ _ _ _ _ _

_ _ _ _ _ _ _ _ _

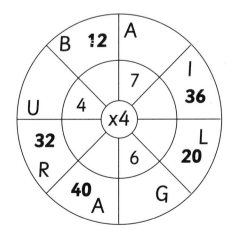

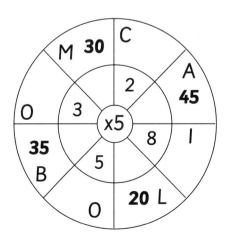

_ _ _ _ _ _ _ _ _

_ _ _ _ _ _ _ _ _

3. Build your own multiplication wheels with these hubs: x3, x7, x9, x10.

This page may be copied (see page 2) © Collins Educational 1992.

Nearly 60

LEVEL	UA	N	A	S	D
1					
2	●				
3	●				
4	●	●			
5					
6					
7					
8					
9					
10					

N4: Adding and subtracting two two-digit numbers
Estimating and approximating to check the vailidity of addition and subtraction calculations

SKILLS
► Adding two-digit numbers
► Finding differences between two-digit numbers

EXTENSION
► Consider any one of these addition sums and find out how many different totals there are. Are there the same number of different totals for the other addition sums?

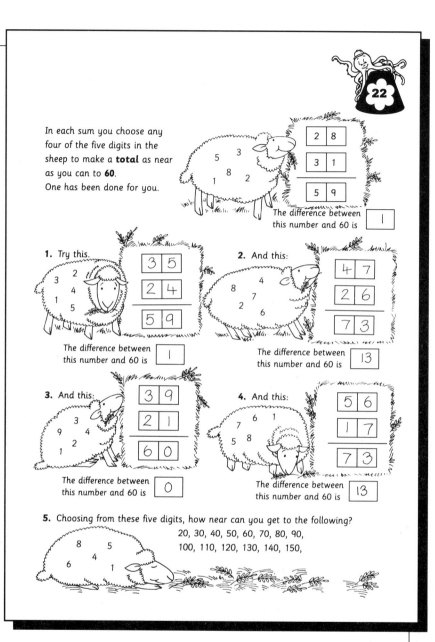

In each sum you choose any four of the five digits in the sheep to make a **total** as near as you can to **60**.
One has been done for you.

2 8
3 1
5 9
The difference between this number and 60 is 1

1. Try this.
3 5
2 4
5 9
The difference between this number and 60 is 1

2. And this:
4 7
2 6
7 3
The difference between this number and 60 is 13

3. And this:
3 9
2 1
6 0
The difference between this number and 60 is 0

4. And this:
5 6
1 7
7 3
The difference between this number and 60 is 13

5. Choosing from these five digits, how near can you get to the following?
20, 30, 40, 50, 60, 70, 80, 90, 100, 110, 120, 130, 140, 150,

SPECTRUM LINKS

	Data Handling	Games	Investigations	Algebra/S&S	Number Skills
Starting			**17** Totals		
More			**25** 4-Card Fun		**7** What's Missing? **36** Differences
Go Further With					**8** Nearly 20 **9** 5-Card Sums **17** Missing Subtractions

Nearly 60

In each sum you choose any four of the five digits in the sheep to make a **total** as near as you can to **60**.
One has been done for you.

2	8
3	1
5	9

The difference between this number and 60 is

1. Try this.

The difference between this number and 60 is

2. And this:

The difference between this number and 60 is

3. And this:

The difference between this number and 60 is

4. And this:

The difference between this number and 60 is

5. Choosing from these five digits, how near can you get to the following?

20, 30, 40, 50, 60, 70, 80, 90,
100, 110, 120, 130, 140, 150,

This page may be copied (see page 2) © Collins Educational 1992. **SPECTRUM MATHS** ▲ MORE NUMBER SKILLS

Three From Four

LEVEL	UA	N	A	S	D
1					
2	●				
3	●	●			
4	●				
5					
6					
7					
8					
9					
10					

N3: Writing and ordering numbers to at least 1000

SKILLS

► Systematic arrangement of three digits from four

APPARATUS

Numbered cards

NOTES

Numbered cards can help children to explore the arrangements systematically, by keeping one or two cards fixed and arranging the others in turn.

Use three of the four digits 1, 2, 5 and 6, to make different **three-digit numbers**. Use each digit once only in a number. Can you write 24 different numbers?

1. Numbers beginning with 1

1	2	5
1	2	6
1	5	2
1	5	6
1	6	2
1	6	5

2. Numbers beginning with 2

2	1	5
2	1	6
2	5	1
2	5	6
2	6	1
2	6	5

3. Numbers beginning with 5

5	1	2
5	1	6
5	2	1
5	2	6
5	6	1
5	6	2

4. Numbers beginning with 6

6	1	2
6	1	5
6	2	1
6	5	2
6	5	1
6	2	5

5. Try with a different set of four digits.

SPECTRUM LINKS

	Data Handling	Games	Investigations	Algebra/S&S	Number Skills
Starting		5 Eight Points 8 Largest 11 Middle It	40 Twos		26 Largest Odd 36 How Near?
More		7 Spot On 13 Brag	1 Numbering 13 Three Digits 16 Near Things		27 Nearest 100 29 Nearest 10

Three From Four

Use three of the four digits 1, 2, 5 and 6, to make different **three-digit numbers**.
Use each digit once only in a number.
Can you write 24 different numbers?

1. Numbers beginning with 1

1	2	5

2. Numbers beginning with 2

3. Numbers beginning with 5

4. Numbers beginning with 6

5. Try with a different set of four digits.

This page may be copied (see page 2) © Collins Educational 1992.

SPECTRUM MATHS ▲ MORE NUMBER SKILLS

Triangle Sums

LEVEL	UA	N	A	S	D
1					
2	●		●		
3	●	●			
4	●				
5					
6					
7					
8					
9					
10					

N3: Learning and using addition and subtraction facts to 20
A2: Understanding the use of a symbol to stand for an unknown number

SKILLS

► Adding and subtracting, involving numbers up to 20

NOTE

Part 2 is more difficult because children will need to experiment by trial and error until they find solutions.

If you add the two numbers in the **circles**, you get the number in the **square** between them, like this ➜

1. Now try these:

2. And these:

SPECTRUM LINKS

	Data Handling	Games	Investigations	Algebra/S&S	Number Skills
More					**9** Triangle Corners
Go Further With					**14** Number Puzzles

Triangle Sums

24

If you add the two numbers
in the **circles**,
you get the number in the
square between them, like this ➡

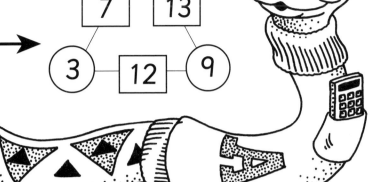

1. Now try these:

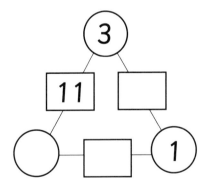

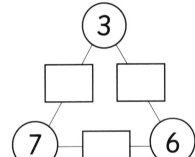

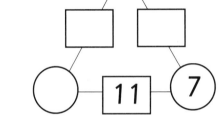

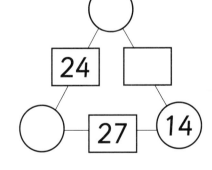

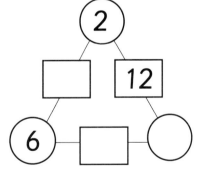

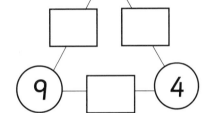

2. And these:

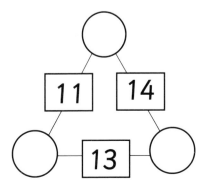

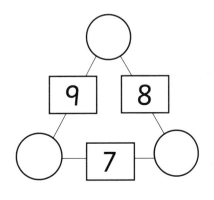

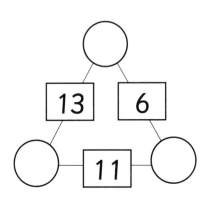

This page may be copied (see page 2) © Collins Educational 1992.

Addition Grids

LEVEL	UA	N	A	S	D
1					
2	●				
3	●	●			
4	●	●			
5					
6					
7					
8					
9					
10					

N3: Addition and subtraction facts
N4: Solving addition and subtraction problems

SKILLS

► Adding and subtracting
► Searching for different arrangements of digits with the same total

APPARATUS

Cards numbered 1 to 9

NOTE

Ask children to draw a large 3 x 3 square, so that their numbered cards can be placed in the grid as they search for different solutions.

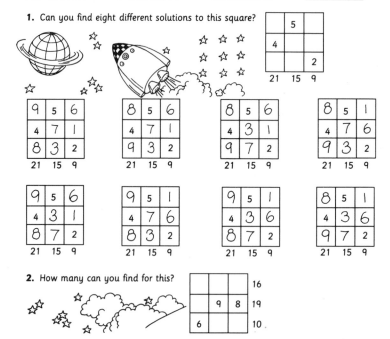

This **3 x 3 square** contains each of the numbers from 1 - 9. Only some are shown.
It also shows the **total** you get when all the numbers in a row are added together. If you fill in the gaps, you will find there are four different solutions:

1. Can you find eight different solutions to this square?

2. How many can you find for this?

SPECTRUM LINKS

	Data Handling	Games	Investigations	Algebra/S&S	Number Skills
More		26 Fifteens			18 2 x 2 Addition Grids 26 Cloud Numbers
Go Further With					2 Magic Squares 22 Place Nine

Addition Grids

9			19
1	5		12
		2	14

This **3 x 3 square** contains each of the numbers from 1 - 9.
Only some are shown.

It also shows the **total** you get when all the numbers
in a row are added together. If you fill in the gaps, you will
find there are four different solutions:

9	7	3	19
1	5	6	12
4	8	2	14

9	3	7	19
1	5	6	12
4	8	2	14

9	7	3	19
1	5	6	12
8	4	2	14

9	3	7	19
1	5	6	12
8	4	2	14

1. Can you find eight different solutions to this square?

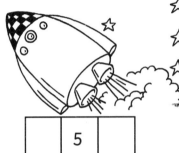

	5	
4		
		2

21　15　9

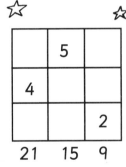

	5	
4		
		2

21　15　9

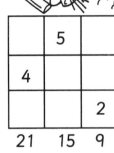

	5	
4		
		2

21　15　9

	5	
4		
		2

21　15　9

	5	
4		
		2

21　15　9

	5	
4		
		2

21　15　9

	5	
4		
		2

21　15　9

	5	
4		
		2

21　15　9

2. How many can you find for this?

			16
	9	8	19
	6		10

This page may be copied (see page 2) © Collins Educational 1992.

Cloud Numbers

LEVEL	UA	N	A	S	D
1					
2					
3					
4		●	●		
5					
6					
7					
8					
9					
10					

N4: Learning multiplication facts up to 10 x 10 and using them in multiplication and division problems

A4: Factors
Recognising that multiplication and division are inverse operations and using this to check calculations

SKILLS

► Multiplying numbers up to 10 x 10
► Division of a two-digit number by a single-digit number
► Recognising factors and common factors

EXTENSION

► Ask children to suggest different possible pairs of sun numbers for given cloud numbers.

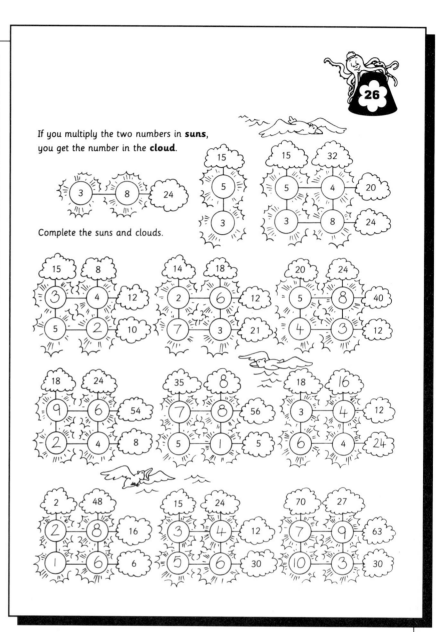

If you multiply the two numbers in **suns**, you get the number in the **cloud**.

Complete the suns and clouds.

SPECTRUM LINKS

	Data Handling	Games	Investigations	Algebra/S&S	Number Skills
More		37 Snake Bite 38 Divido	6 Table Patterns 7 Pick Your Cards 8 Table Ends	8 Completing Rectangles 12 Sift the Multiples 13 Table Patterns	16 Factor Pairs
Go Further With		13 Race Track 20 Factor 24 Multiple Choice	9 Factors 13 Tables	4 Prime Numbers 17 Factor Graph 18 Multiplication Machines	11 Lowest Common Multiples 12 Factor Show 18 Factor Grids 25 Highest Common Factors

Cloud Numbers

26

If you multiply the two numbers in **suns**,
you get the number in the **cloud**.

Complete the suns and clouds.

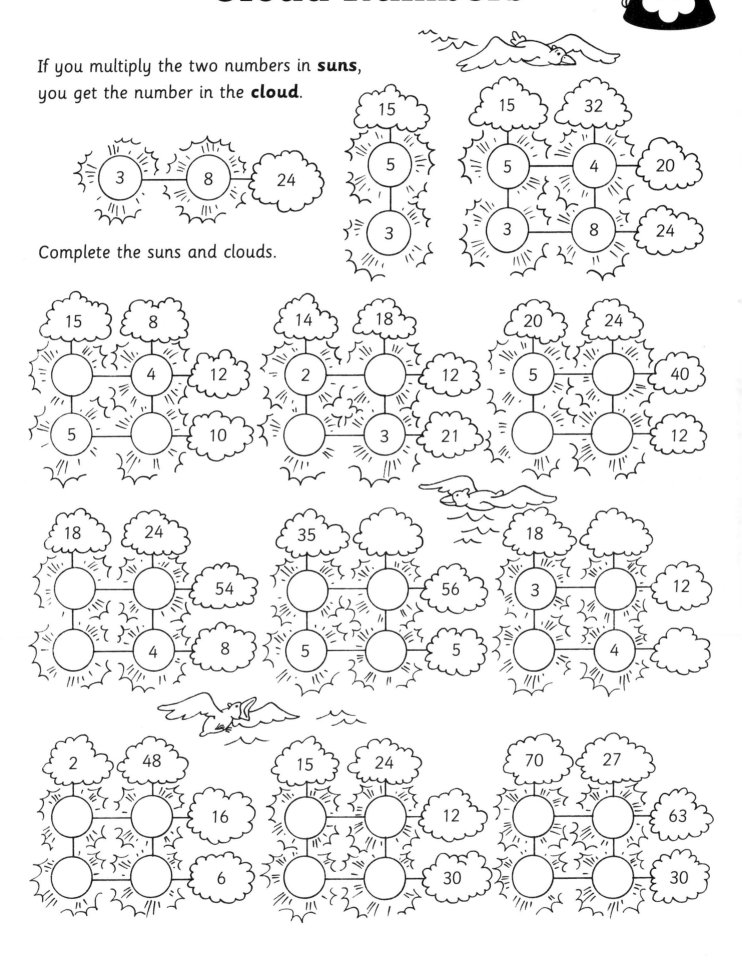

This page may be copied (see page 2) © Collins Educational 1992.

Nearest 100

LEVEL	UA	N	A	S	D
1					
2	●				
3	●	●			
4	●				
5					
6					
7					
8					
9					
10					

N3: Ordering numbers to at least 1000

SKILLS

► Writing three- and five-digit numbers to the nearest hundred
► Reading a linear scale

EXTENSIONS

► Ask the children to express the numbers in questions 2, 3 and 4 to the nearest 10.
► Further data on football match attendances is available in Sunday newspapers. Children could use these in rounding exercises, to the nearest 100 or the nearest 10.

In these activities, you must write numbers **to the nearest 100**.
In the first three activities the first one has been done for you.

1. Write the numbers to the nearest 100.

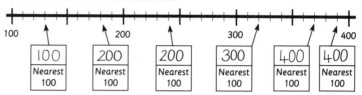

100	200	200	300	400	400
Nearest 100	Nearest 100	Nearest 100	Nearest 100	Nearest 100	Nearest 100

2. Write the number of miles, to the nearest 100.

Table showing distances of towns from Ourtown

Town	Distance from (in miles)	Distance to the nearest 100 miles
Aberdeen	331	300
Bristol	157	200
Coventry	94	100
Exeter	230	200
Dover	251	300
Inverness	364	400
Holyhead	123	100
Fishguard	196	200
Cardiff	171	200
Gloucester	122	100

3. Write the number of people, to the nearest 100.

Table showing attendances at football matches, Saturday, May 2nd '92

Match	Attendance	nearest 100
Arsenal 5 Southampton 1	37,702	37,700
Aston Villa 2 Coventry 0	31,984	32,000
Everton 2 Chelsea 1	20,163	20,200
Leeds 1 Norwich 0	32,673	32,700
Man. Utd 3 Tottenham 1	44,595	44,600
Notts. C. 2 2 Luton 1	11,380	11,400
Oldham 2 Man. City 5	18,588	18,600

4. Make different three-digit numbers with 3, 6, 4. and write them **to the nearest 100**.

Question 4: 346 ► 300; 364 ► 400; 436 ► 400; 463 ► 500; 634 ► 600; 643 ► 600.

SPECTRUM LINKS

	Data Handling	Games	Investigations	Algebra/S&S	Number Skills
Starting					27 Number Lines
More	39 Third Division	4 Smallest 9 Six Choices 13 Brag	1 Numbering		11 Temperature Scales 29 Nearest 10
Go Further With					4 Tenths

Nearest 100

In these activities, you must write numbers **to the nearest 100**.
In the first three activities the first one has been done for you.

1. Write the numbers to the nearest 100.

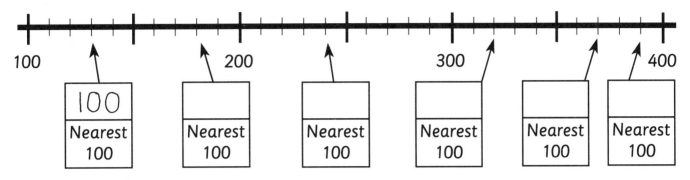

100					
Nearest 100	Nearest 100	Nearest 100	Nearest 100	Nearest 100	Nearest 100

2. Write the number of miles, to the nearest 100.

Table showing distances of towns from Ourtown		
Town	Distance from (in miles)	Distance to the nearest 100 miles
Aberdeen	331	300
Bristol	157	
Coventry	94	
Exeter	230	
Dover	251	
Inverness	364	
Holyhead	123	
Fishguard	196	
Cardiff	171	
Gloucester	122	

3. Write the number of people, to the nearest 100.

Table showing attendances at football matches, Saturday, May 2nd '92		
Match	Attendance	nearest 100
Arsenal 5 Southampton 1	37,702	37,700
Aston Villa 2 Coventry 0	31,984	
Everton 2 Chelsea 1	20,163	
Leeds 1 Norwich 0	32,673	
Man. Utd 3 Tottenham 1	44,595	
Notts. C. 2 2 Luton 1	11,380	
Oldham 2 Man. City 5	18,588	

4. Make different three-digit numbers with 3, 6, 4.
and write them **to the nearest 100**.

Arch Numbers

LEVEL	UA	N	A	S	D
1					
2	●				
3	●	●			
4	●	●	●		
5					
6					
7					
8					
9					
10					

N3/4: Addition, subtraction, multiplication and division
A4: Understanding and using simple equations

SKILLS

► Writing expressions for numbers using combinations of the operations of addition, subtraction, multiplication and division

EXTENSION

► Children can build another arch which is numbered from 19 to 36, and try to fill the bricks using the same digits.

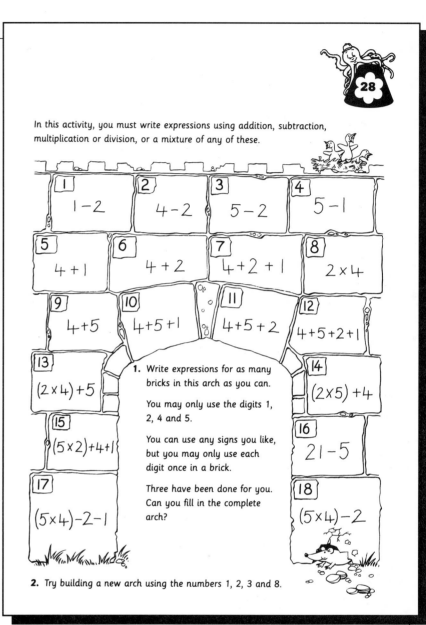

In this activity, you must write expressions using addition, subtraction, multiplication or division, or a mixture of any of these.

1. | 1 - 2 |
2. | 4 - 2 |
3. | 5 - 2 |
4. | 5 - 1 |
5. | 4 + 1 |
6. | 4 + 2 |
7. | 4 + 2 + 1 |
8. | 2 × 4 |
9. | 4 + 5 |
10. | 4 + 5 + 1 |
11. | 4 + 5 + 2 |
12. | 4 + 5 + 2 + 1 |
13. | (2 × 4) + 5 |
14. | (2 × 5) + 4 |
15. | (5 × 2) + 4 + 1 |
16. | 21 - 5 |
17. | (5 × 4) - 2 - 1 |
18. | (5 × 4) - 2 |

1. Write expressions for as many bricks in this arch as you can.

You may only use the digits 1, 2, 4 and 5.

You can use any signs you like, but you may only use each digit once in a brick.

Three have been done for you. Can you fill in the complete arch?

2. Try building a new arch using the numbers 1, 2, 3 and 8.

SPECTRUM LINKS

	Data Handling	Games	Investigations	Algebra/S&S	Number Skills
Starting		13 Big Match 18 Summary 27 Choosy	10 Trios 12 Keep your Balance 14 Card Tricks	6 Shape Search 10 Stroking Cats 15 Hunt the Numbers	
More		3 Boxer 8 Dice Superstars	29 Asking Questions	10 Mystery People	15 Dice Lines 20 Equation Solving 31 Target Practice
Go Further With		8 A Mouthful 33 Challenge 38 Switch	16 Number Nine 21 Equations 33 Signs	7 Number Tricks 10 Think of a Number 14 Whodunnit?	6 Countdown 7 Mixed Equations 13 Three Spots 15 A Special Date

Arch Numbers

In this activity, you must write expressions using addition, subtraction, multiplication or division, or a mixture of any of these.

| 1 | 2 | 3 | 4 $5 - 1$ |

| 5 | 6 | 7 $4 + 2 + 1$ | 8 |

9   10   11   12

13   14

1. Write expressions for as many bricks in this arch as you can.

You may only use the digits 1, 2, 4 and 5.

You can use any signs you like, but you may only use each digit once in a brick.

Three have been done for you. Can you fill in the complete arch?

15   16 $21 - 5$

17   18

2. Try building a new arch using the numbers 1, 2, 3 and 8.

This page may be copied (see page 2) © Collins Educational 1992.

Nearest 10

29

LEVEL	UA	N	A	S	D
1					
2	●	●			
3	●	●			
4	●			●	
5					
6					
7					
8					
9					
10					

N2: Ordering numbers to at least 100
N3: Using appropriate units and instruments; interpreting numbers on a range of measuring instruments
Approximating to the nearest 10
S4: Finding perimeters of simple shapes

SKILLS

► Writing two-digit numbers to the nearest 10
► Reading a linear scale
► Measuring lengths in millimetres

NOTE

Ask the children to estimate the lengths in millimetres before measuring them.

EXTENSION

Ask the children to draw their own shapes, measure the lines along the sides and write down the measurements to the nearest 10mm.

In these activities, you must write a number **to the nearest 10**.
In the first two activities the first one has been done for you.

1. Write the numbers to the nearest 10.

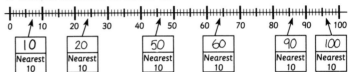

10	20	50	60	90	100
Nearest 10	Nearest 10	Nearest 10	Nearest 10	Nearest 10	Nearest 10

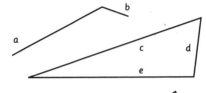

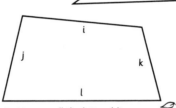

Line	Length in mm	Length to nearest 10 mm
a	53mm	50mm
b	14mm	20mm
c	94mm	90mm
d	38mm	40mm
e	67mm	70mm
f	58mm	60mm
g	34mm	30mm
h	62mm	60mm
i	63mm	60mm
j	44mm	40mm
k	39mm	40mm
l	83mm	80mm

2. Measure all the lettered lines.
Fill in the table to show exactly how long each line is, and how long it is to the nearest 10 mm.

3. What are the perimeters of the shapes, exactly?
What are the perimeters to the nearest 10 mm?
Write your answers inside the shapes.

Question 3: perimetres are: $a + b$ = 67mm (70mm);
$c + d + e$ = 199mm (200mm); $f + g + h$ = 154mm (150mm);
$i + j + k + l$ = 229mm (230mm)

SPECTRUM LINKS

	Data Handling	Games	Investigations	Algebra/S&S	Number Skills
Starting		**5** Eight Points **8** Largest **11** Middle it	**40** Twos		**27** Number Lines
More		**7** Spot On	**16** Near Things		**11** Temperature Scales **27** Nearest 100
Go Further With					**4** Tenths

Nearest 10

In these activities, you must write a number **to the nearest 10**.
In the first two activities the first one has been done for you.

1. Write the numbers to the nearest 10.

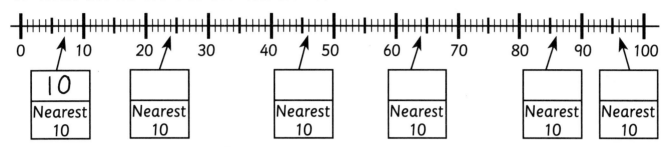

10					
Nearest 10	Nearest 10	Nearest 10	Nearest 10	Nearest 10	Nearest 10

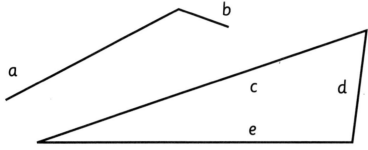

Line	Length in mm	Length to nearest 10 mm
a	53mm	50mm
b		
c		
d		
e		
f		
g		
h		
i		
j		
k		
l		

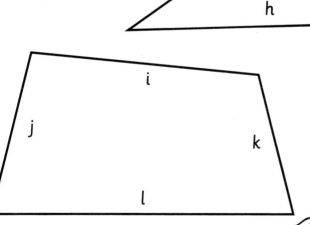

2. Measure all the lettered lines.
Fill in the table to show exactly how long each line is,
and how long it is to the nearest 10 mm.

3. What are the perimeters of the shapes, exactly?
What are the perimeters to the nearest 10 mm?
Write your answers inside the shapes.

This page may be copied (see page 2) © Collins Educational 1992.   **SPECTRUM MATHS** ▲ **MORE NUMBER SKILLS**

Octagon Puzzle

LEVEL	UA	N	A	S	D
1					
2	●				
3	●	●	●		
4	●	●			
5					
6					
7					
8					
9					
10					

N3: Learning and using addition and subtraction facts to 20
N4: Learning multiplication facts up to 10 x 10 and using them in multiplication and division problems
A3: Explaining number patterns and predicting subsequent numbers

SKILLS

► Multiplying single-digit numbers
► Adding two-digit numbers

APPARATUS

Special Paper 3

NOTES

The numbers in the octagon on the left are multiplied by another number (call it *a*) to make the numbers in the top octagon. They are multiplied by *b* to make the numbers in the bottom octagon. The octagon on the right could be filled in directly by multiplying the numbers in the left-hand octagon by *a* + *b*.

EXTENSION

► Use Special Paper 3 for children to invent their own puzzles.

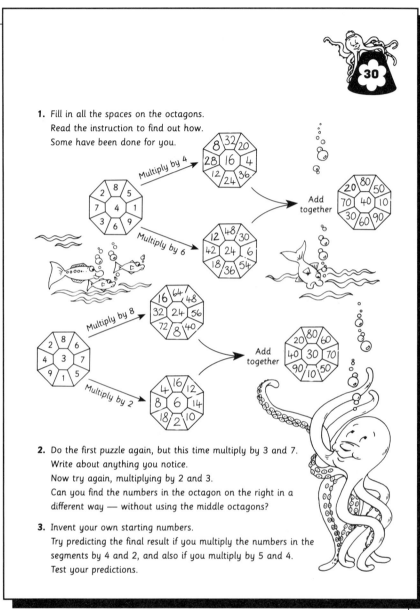

1. Fill in all the spaces on the octagons. Read the instruction to find out how. Some have been done for you.

2. Do the first puzzle again, but this time multiply by 3 and 7. Write about anything you notice.
   Now try again, multiplying by 2 and 3.
   Can you find the numbers in the octagon on the right in a different way — without using the middle octagons?

3. Invent your own starting numbers.
   Try predicting the final result if you multiply the numbers in the segments by 4 and 2, and also if you multiply by 5 and 4. Test your predictions.

Question 2: multiply each number in the left hand octagon by 10 (6 + 4 or 8 + 2) and you will get the numbers to fill in the right hand octagon.

SPECTRUM LINKS

	Data Handling	Games	Investigations	Algebra/S&S	Number Skills
Starting					29 Hexagon Puzzle

Octagon Puzzle

1. Fill in all the spaces on the octagons.
Read the instruction to find out how.
Some have been done for you.

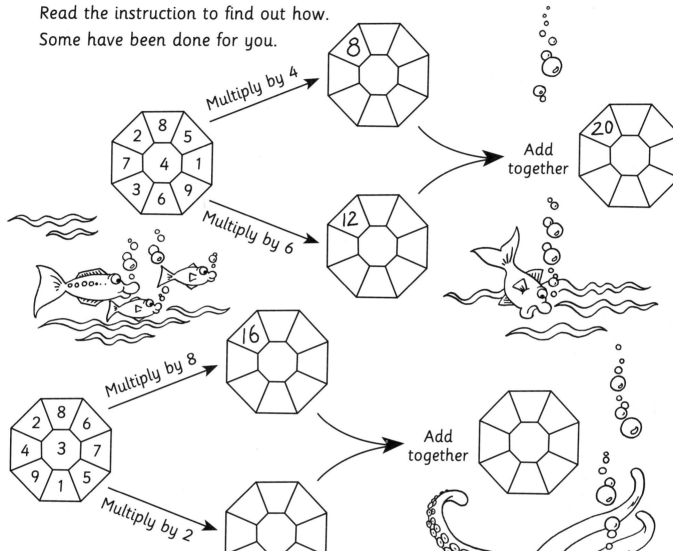

2. Do the first puzzle again, but this time multiply by 3 and 7.
Write about anything you notice.
Now try again, multiplying by 2 and 3.
Can you find the numbers in the octagon on the right in a
different way — without using the middle octagons?

3. Invent your own starting numbers.
Try predicting the final result if you multiply the numbers in the
segments by 4 and 2, and also if you multiply by 5 and 4.
Test your predictions.

This page may be copied (see page 2) © Collins Educational 1992.

Target Practice

LEVEL	UA	N	A	S	D
1					
2	●				
3	●	●			
4	●	●	●		
5					
6					
7					
8					
9					
10					

N3: Learning and using addition and subtraction facts to 20
N4: Learning multiplication facts up to 10 x 10 and using them in multiplication and division problems
A4: Understanding and using simple equations

SKILLS

► Writing expressions using three digits and number operations

EXTENSION

► With a given set of arrows, explore how many different targets can be hit exactly (that is, SCORE: 0)

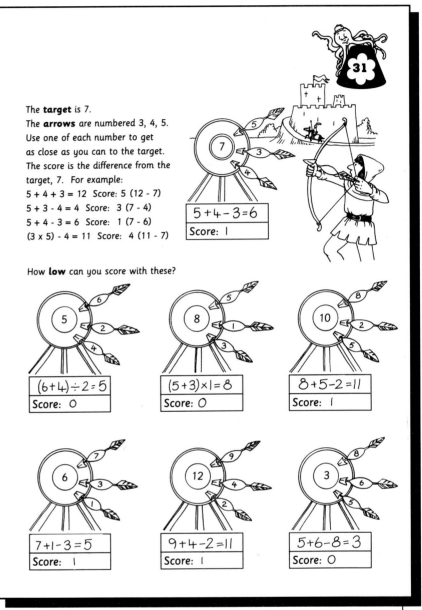

The **target** is 7.
The **arrows** are numbered 3, 4, 5.
Use one of each number to get as close as you can to the target.
The score is the difference from the target, 7. For example:
5 + 4 + 3 = 12 Score: 5 (12 - 7)
5 + 3 - 4 = 4 Score: 3 (7 - 4)
5 + 4 - 3 = 6 Score: 1 (7 - 6)
(3 x 5) - 4 = 11 Score: 4 (11 - 7)

5 + 4 - 3 = 6
Score: 1

How **low** can you score with these?

(6 + 4) ÷ 2 = 5
Score: 0

(5 + 3) × 1 = 8
Score: 0

8 + 5 - 2 = 11
Score: 1

7 + 1 - 3 = 5
Score: 1

9 + 4 - 2 = 11
Score: 1

5 + 6 - 8 = 3
Score: 0

SPECTRUM LINKS

	Data Handling	Games	Investigations	Algebra/S&S	Number Skills
Starting		13 Big Match 18 Summary 27 Choosy	10 Trios 12 Keep Your Balance 14 Card Tricks	6 Shape Search 10 Stroking Cats 15 Hunt the Numbers	
More		3 Boxer 8 Dice Superstars	29 Asking Questions	10 Mystery People	15 Dice Lines 20 Equation Solving 28 Arch Numbers
Go Further With		8 A Mouthful 33 Challenge 38 Switch	16 Number Nine 21 Equations 33 Signs	7 Number Tricks 10 Think of a Number 14 Whodunnit?	6 Countdown 7 Mixed Equations 13 Three Spots 15 A Special Date

Equation Puzzles

These squares can be filled in, using addition and subtraction.

1. Write numbers in each empty square, to make all the **equations** true.

20	+	4	=	
−		−		−
	+	2	=	
=		=		=
17	+		=	

	+	7	=	35
−		−		−
5	+		=	
=		=		=
	+	1	=	

16	−		=	7
+		+		+
	−	2	=	
=		=		=
	−		=	10

	+		=	
−		+		−
	−	9	=	6
=		=		=
6	+	13	=	

13	−		=	
+		−		+
2	+		=	3
=		=		=
	−		=	7

	−	6	=	
+		+		+
	−		=	6
=		=		=
28	−		=	18

2. Try inventing your own **equation puzzle**.

This page may be copied (see page 2) © Collins Educational 1992.   **SPECTRUM MATHS** ▲ MORE NUMBER SKILLS

The Right Boxes

LEVEL	UA	N	A	S	D
1					
2	●		●		●
3	●				
4	●		●		
5					
6					
7					
8					
9					
10					

A2: Distinguishing odd and even numbers
A4: Multiples
D2: Using diagrams to represent the result of classification using two different criteria

SKILLS

► Sorting numbers into sets of different types of numbers

APPARATUS

Numbered cards

NOTES

Before children begin this activity, discuss the numbers that belong in each of these sets. They may have to use trial and error to solve the problem of deciding which numbers go in which boxes: some will fit into more than one, yet the boxes must end up with only three numbers in each. Use numbered cards to try out ideas.

Sort the numbers into the right boxes. Each box must have **three** numbers. One has been done for you.

Numbers between 5 and 11	Odd numbers	
7 9 10	13 5 3	

1. Try sorting these. Use numbered cards to help you.

Numbers between 8 and 13	Multiples of 3	Odd numbers
9 10 11	3 6 12	7 13 5

Multiples of 2	Multiples of 3	Multiples of 4
14 10 6	3 15 24	4 12 8

Even numbers	Odd numbers	Factors of 12
8 10 16	5 7 9	6 3 4

Odd numbers	Prime numbers	Square numbers
27 15 21	3 11 5	4 9 25

Numbers less than 6	Multiples of 6	Numbers more than 9	Even numbers
2 5 4	6 18 12	17 15 11	10 14 8

	Odd Numbers	Multiples of 3
Numbers less than 10	5 1 7	3 6 9
Numbers more than 10	11 13 17	12 18 15

SPECTRUM LINKS

	Data Handling	Games	Investigations	Algebra/S&S	Number Skills
Starting					**1** Streets **14** Fruit Gums **23** Sorting Numbers
Go Further With					**11** Lowest Common Multiples

The Right Boxes

Sort the numbers into the right boxes.
Each box must have **three** numbers.
One has been done for you.

Numbers: 10, 13, 7, 5, 3, 9

Numbers between 5 and 11	Odd numbers
7 9 10	13 5 3

1. Try sorting these. Use numbered cards to help you.

Numbers: 9, 5, 3, 6, 3, 12, 11, 7, 10

Numbers between 8 and 13	Multiples of 3	Odd numbers

Numbers: 6, 24, 4, 14, 15, 8, 12, 10, 3

Multiples of 2	Multiples of 3	Multiples of 4

Numbers: 16, 9, 4, 5, 3, 8, 6, 7, 10

Even numbers	Odd numbers	Factors of 12

Numbers: 11, 15, 21, 4, 25, 27, 5, 9, 3

Odd numbers	Prime numbers	Square numbers

Numbers: 10, 18, 2, 15, 12, 4, 14, 8, 17, 5, 11, 6

Numbers less than 6	Multiples of 6	Numbers more than 9	Even numbers

Numbers: 18, 5, 3, 15, 6, 12, 17, 11, 13, 7, 9

	Odd Numbers	Multiples of 3
Numbers less than 10		
Numbers more than 10		

This page may be copied (see page 2) © Collins Educational 1992.

Magic Windmills

LEVEL	UA	N	A	S	D
1					
2		●			
3		●			
4					
5					
6					
7					
8					
9					
10					

N2/3: Learning and using addition and subtraction facts to 20

SKILLS

► Adding three single-digit numbers
► Selecting numbers to make a given total

APPARATUS

Numbered cards, 1-9

NOTE

The children can draw a large windmill on paper, then arrange the given numbered cards on the windmill to help them find a solution to each puzzle.

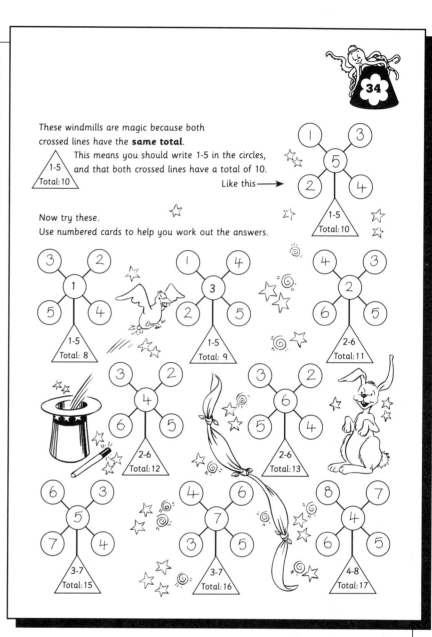

SPECTRUM LINKS

	Data Handling	Games	Investigations	Algebra/S&S	Number Skills
Starting			**23** Dice Sort		
More		**26** Fifteens	**2** Lucky 13 **11** Triplets		**25** Addition Grids **35** Magic Triangles **38** Side Totals
Go Further With					**1** The Big Wheel

Magic Windmills

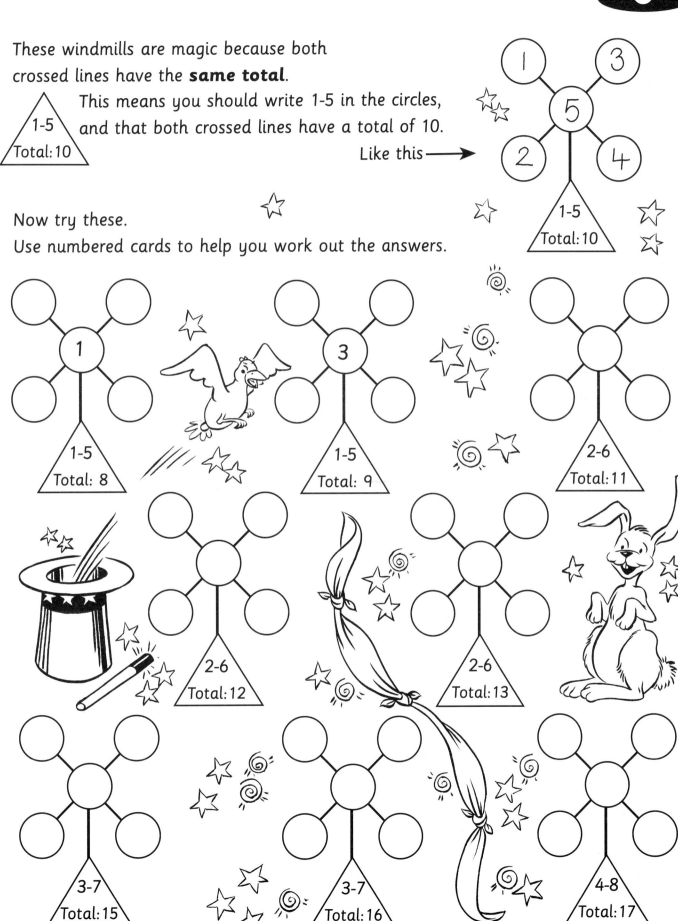

These windmills are magic because both crossed lines have the **same total**.

This means you should write 1-5 in the circles, and that both crossed lines have a total of 10.

Like this ⟶

1-5
Total: 10

Now try these.
Use numbered cards to help you work out the answers.

1-5
Total: 10

1
1-5
Total: 8

3
1-5
Total: 9

2-6
Total: 11

2-6
Total: 12

2-6
Total: 13

3-7
Total: 15

3-7
Total: 16

4-8
Total: 17

35

Magic Triangles

LEVEL	UA	N	A	S	D
1					
2		●			
3		●			
4					
5					
6					
7					
8					
9					
10					

N2/3: Learning and using addition and subtraction facts

SKILLS
► Adding three single-digit numbers
► Selecting numbers to make a given total

APPARATUS
Numbered cards, 1-10

NOTES
The children can draw a large triangle on paper, then arrange the numbered cards on the triangle, to help them find solutions for each puzzle.

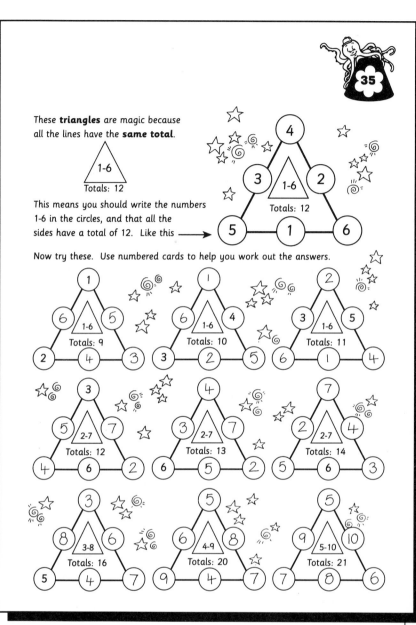

SPECTRUM LINKS

	Data Handling	Games	Investigations	Algebra/S&S	Number Skills
Starting			**23** Dice Sort		
More		**26** Fifteens	**2** Lucky 13 **11** Triplets		**25** Addition Grids **34** Magic Windmills **38** Side Totals
Go Further With					**1** The Big Wheel

Magic Triangles

These **triangles** are magic because all the lines have the **same total**.

1-6
Totals: 12

This means you should write the numbers 1-6 in the circles, and that all the sides have a total of 12. Like this ➞

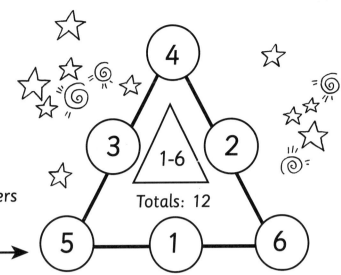

Now try these. Use numbered cards to help you work out the answers.

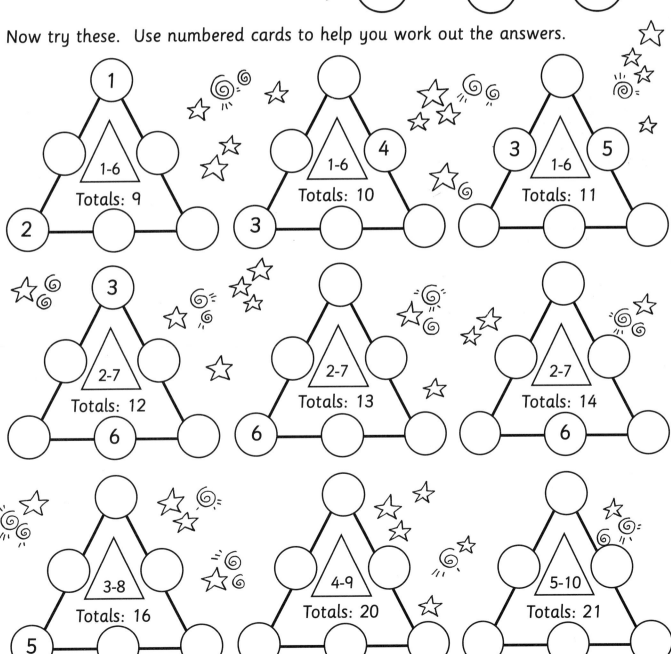

This page may be copied (see page 2) © Collins Educational 1992.

Differences

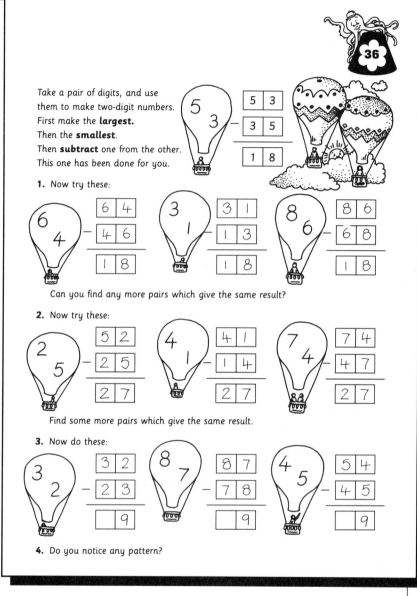

Take a pair of digits, and use them to make two-digit numbers. First make the **largest.** Then the **smallest.** Then **subtract** one from the other. This one has been done for you.

5 3

5	3

−

3	5

1	8

1. Now try these:

6 4

6	4

−

4	6

1	8

3 1

3	1

−

1	3

1	8

8 6

8	6

−

6	8

1	8

Can you find any more pairs which give the same result?

2. Now try these:

2 5

5	2

−

2	5

2	7

4 1

4	1

−

1	4

2	7

7 4

7	4

−

4	7

2	7

Find some more pairs which give the same result.

3. Now do these:

3 2

3	2

−

2	3

	9

8 7

8	7

−

7	8

	9

4 5

5	4

−

4	5

	9

4. Do you notice any pattern?

SKILLS

► Subtracting two-digit numbers

EXTENSION

► Ask the children to throw two dice and then see if they can predict the difference between the largest and smallest two-digit numbers made with the dice numbers.

LEVEL	UA	N	A	S	D
1					
2	●				
3	●				
4	●	●	●		
5					
6					
7					
8					
9					
10					

N4: Adding and subtracting two two-digit numbers
A4: Number patterns

Question 4: in any calculation of this kind, the result will always be a multiple of nine: 9, 18, 27, 36 and so on. The actual multiple depends on whether the differences between the two digits is 1, 2, 3, 4, and so on.

SPECTRUM LINKS

	Data Handling	Games	Investigations	Algebra/S&S	Number Skills
Starting			17 Totals		
More			25 4-Card Fun		7 What's Missing? 22 Nearly 60
Go Further With					8 Nearly 20 9 5-Card Sums 17 Missing Subtractions

Differences

36

Take a pair of digits, and use them to make two-digit numbers.
First make the **largest.**
Then the **smallest.**
Then **subtract** one from the other.
This one has been done for you.

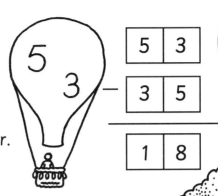

5	3
3	5
1	8

1. Now try these:

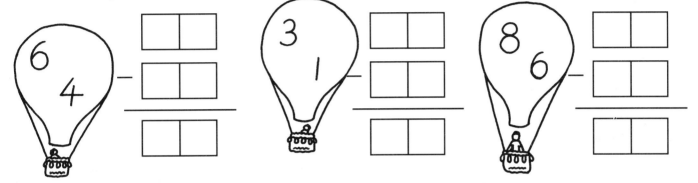

Can you find any more pairs which give the same result?

2. Now try these:

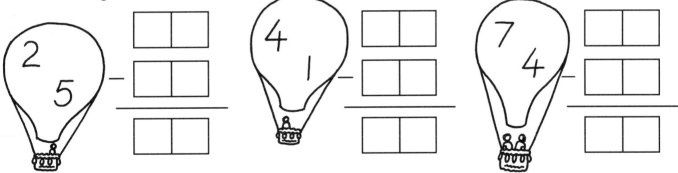

Find some more pairs which give the same result.

3. Now do these:

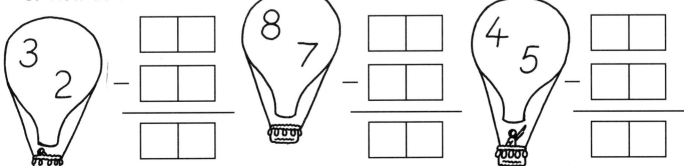

4. Do you notice any pattern?

This page may be copied (see page 2) © Collins Educational 1992.

Addition Pyramids

LEVEL	UA	N	A	S	D
1					
2	●	●			
3	●	●			
4	●	●			
5					
6					
7					
8					
9					
10					

N2/3: Learning and using addition and subtraction facts
N4: Adding several single-digit numbers
Adding and subtracting two two-digit numbers

SKILLS

► Adding pairs of numbers (single- and two-digit numbers)

APPARATUS

Special Paper 5

NOTE

Children can use Special Paper 5 to make their addition pyramids.

EXTENSION

► Invite children to investigate the different possible numbers on the top brick, for different positions of the same digits (for example 1, 2, 3, 4) on the bottom layer.

Addition pyramids are built like this →
Each number is the total of the two below it.

So, this pyramid becomes

1. Build these pyramids.

2. Invent some addition pyramids of your own.

SPECTRUM LINKS

	Data Handling	Games	Investigations	Algebra/S&S	Number Skills
Starting					**40** Difference Pyramids
Go Further With			**4** Top Brick **7** Up the Wall		**39** Decimal Pyramids

Addition Pyramids

Addition pyramids are built like this →
Each number is the total of the two below it.

So, this pyramid becomes

1. Build these pyramids.

2. Invent some addition pyramids of your own.

This page may be copied (see page 2) © Collins Educational 1992.

SPECTRUM MATHS ▲ MORE NUMBER SKILLS

Side Totals

LEVEL	UA	N	A	S	D
1					
2	●				
3	●				
4	●	●			
5					
6					
7					
8					
9					
10					

N4: Adding mentally several single-digit numbers

SKILLS

► Adding four single-digit numbers
► Selecting sets of numbers which add to a given total

APPARATUS

Numbered cards 1-9

NOTES

The puzzles are quite difficult. They can be made easier by giving one or two extra clues.

Children will need the numbered cards to arrange on a large triangle.

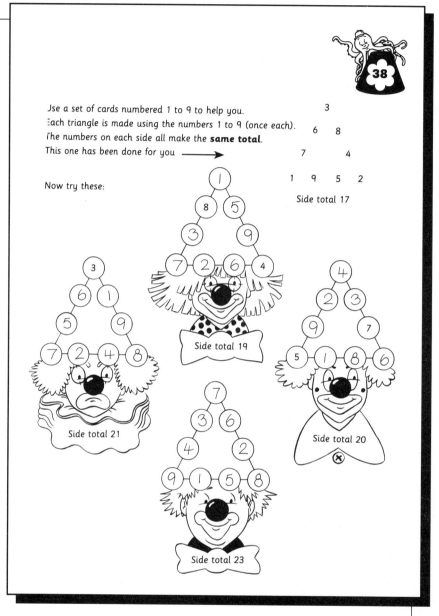

SPECTRUM LINKS

	Data Handling	Games	Investigations	Algebra/S&S	Number Skills
Starting			23 Dice Sort		
More		26 Fifteens	2 Lucky 13 11 Triplets		25 Addition Grids 34 Magic Windmills 35 Magic Triangles
Go Further With					1 The Big Wheel

Side Totals

38

Use a set of cards numbered 1 to 9 to help you.

Each triangle is made using the numbers 1 to 9 (once each).

The numbers on each side all make the **same total**.

This one has been done for you ⟶

```
        3
     6     8
   7          4
 1   9   5   2
```

Side total 17

Now try these:

Side total 19

Side total 21

Side total 20

Side total 23

This page may be copied (see page 2) © Collins Educational 1992.

Grid Pairs

LEVEL	UA	N	A	S	D
1					
2					
3		●			
4			●		
5					
6					
7					
8					
9					
10					

N3: Learning multiplication facts up to 5 x 5
A4: Factors

SKILLS

► Multiplying two single-digit numbers (up to 5 x 5)
► Finding two numbers which have a given product

APPARATUS

Squared paper

NOTE

Occasionally, there is more than one possible pair making the number requested.

EXTENSION

► Invite children to follow up this activity by drawing their own cross on squared paper. They can then make grid pairs puzzles for their friends.

SPECTRUM LINKS

	Data Handling	Games	Investigations	Algebra/S&S	Number Skills
Starting			35 In the Window		4 Giraffe 12 Difference Dog 14 Elephant Tricks
More					19 Twenties
Go Further With					23 Multiples of 10 26 Hexanimals

Grid Pairs

39

This means - find a **vertical pair** of numbers which multiply to make 8.

Example:

2
4	8

This means - find a **horizontal pair** of numbers which multiply to make 5.

Example:

| 5 | 1 | 5

2	1
1	1

3	1	5	2	4	3
2	4	2	4	1	3
4	5	3	4	3	5

5	2
5	1

Find these pairs in the grid:

| | | 10   (vertical) 6   (horizontal) 12   (vertical) 4   (horizontal) 8 |

Find these pairs in the grid:

10

6

12

4

8

15

15

2

4

16

20

25

1

9

3

This page may be copied (see page 2) © Collins Educational 1992.

SPECTRUM MATHS ▲ MORE NUMBER SKILLS

Which Truck?

LEVEL	UA	N	A	S	D
1					
2	●				
3	●				
4	●	●			
5					
6					
7					
8					
9					
10					

N4: Multiplying and dividing two-digit numbers by a single-digit numbers

SKILLS

► Estimating the results of multiplying a two-digit number by a single-digit number

APPARATUS

Calculator

NOTES

After guessing, the accurate multiplication can first be attempted without a calculator, then checked with a calculator.

EXTENSION

► Extend the activity by multiplying together two two-digit numbers. Invite children to attempt to guess the result to within 30 of the accurate result.

The answer to the **multiplication** on each engine is on one of its three trucks.

1. Guess which truck on the first train has the correct answer, and tick the truck. Then multiply the two numbers on the engine together and colour the correct truck. Do the same for all the other trains.

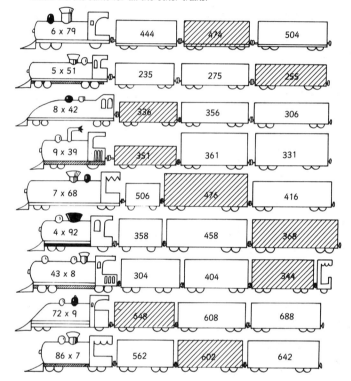

Engine	Truck 1	Truck 2	Truck 3
6 x 79	444	474	504
5 x 51	235	275	255
8 x 42	336	356	306
9 x 39	351	361	331
7 x 68	506	476	416
4 x 92	358	458	368
43 x 8	304	404	344
72 x 9	648	608	688
86 x 7	562	602	642

2. Invent ten more train puzzles like these and try them out on a friend. Work out the answers first.

SPECTRUM LINKS

	Data Handling	Games	Investigations	Algebra/S&S	Number Skills
Go Further With			**29** Elevenses **36** Hard Times		**13** Subtraction Guessing **38** Take Your Pick

Which Truck?

The answer to the **multiplication** on each engine is on one of its three trucks.

1. Guess which truck on the first train has the correct answer, and tick the truck.
   Then multiply the two numbers on the engine together and colour the correct
   truck. Do the same for all the other trains.

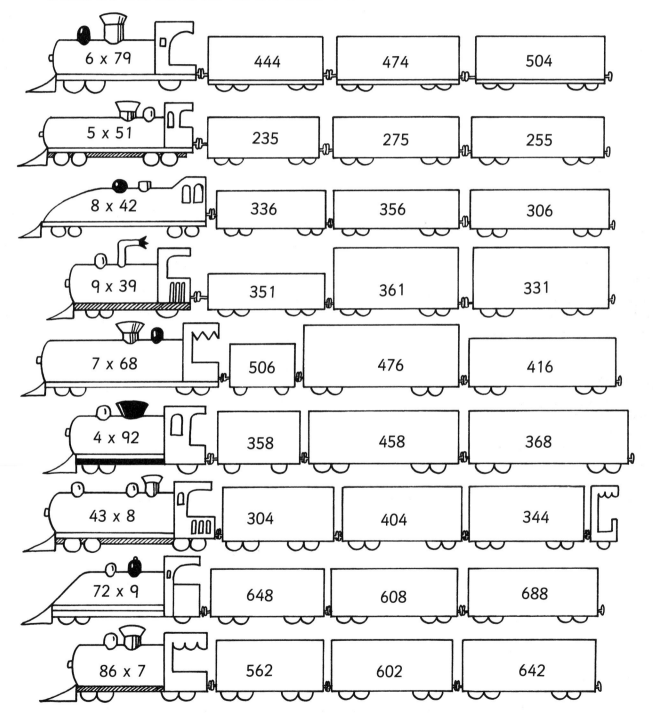

Engine			
6 x 79	444	474	504
5 x 51	235	275	255
8 x 42	336	356	306
9 x 39	351	361	331
7 x 68	506	476	416
4 x 92	358	458	368
43 x 8	304	404	344
72 x 9	648	608	688
86 x 7	562	602	642

2. Invent ten more train puzzles like these and try them out on a friend.
   Work out the answers first.

This page may be copied (see page 2) © Collins Educational 1992.   **SPECTRUM MATHS** ▲ MORE NUMBER SKILLS

Special paper 1

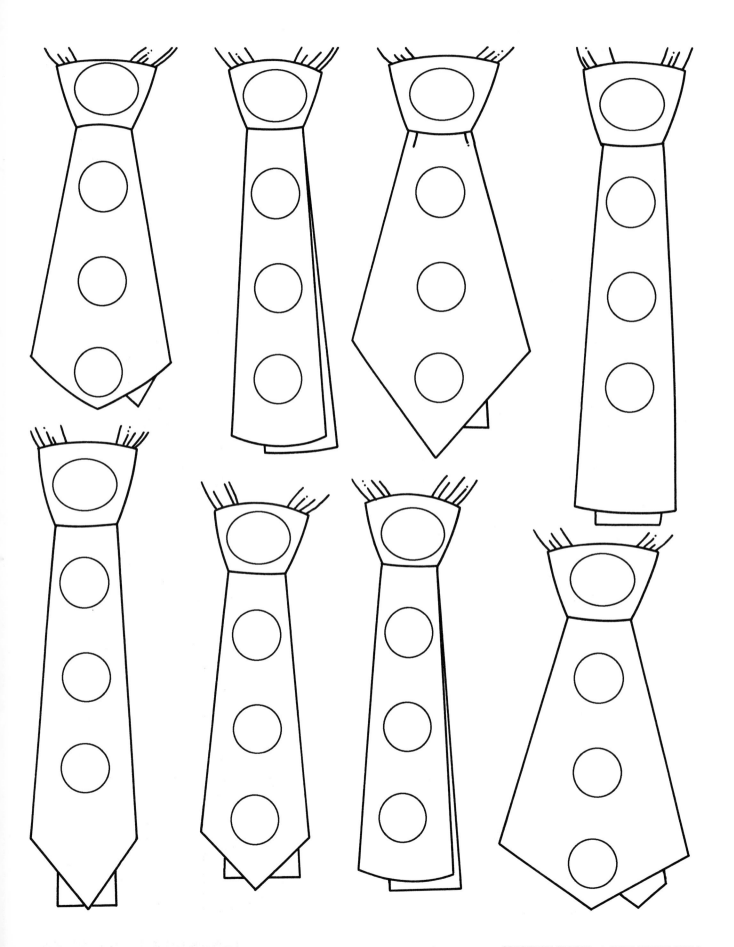

This page may be copied (see page 2) © Collins Educational 1992.

Special paper 2

This page may be copied (see page 2) © Collins Educational 1992.

Special paper 3

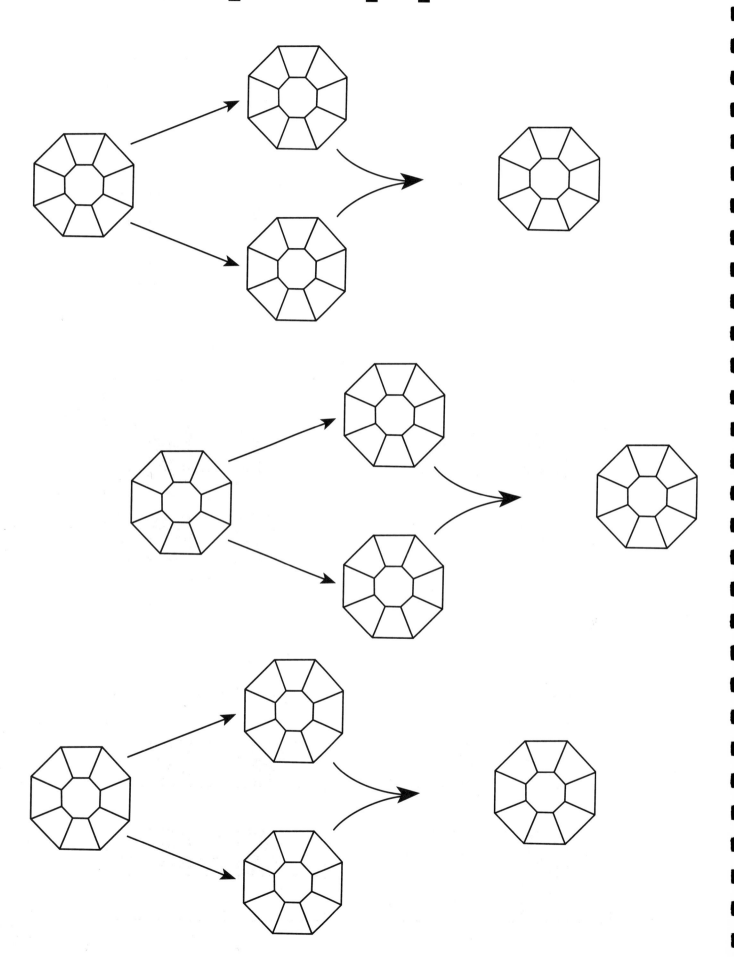

This page may be copied (see page 2) © Collins Educational 1992.

SPECTRUM MATHS ▲ MORE NUMBER SKILLS

Special paper 4

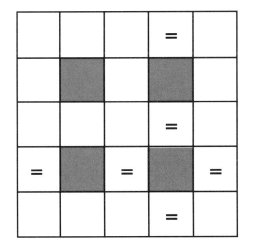

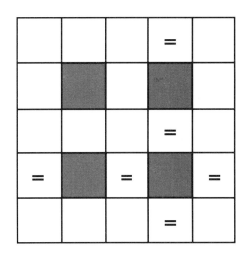

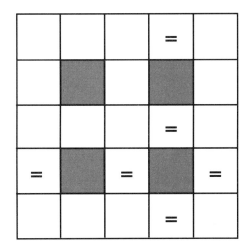

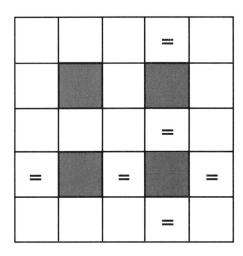

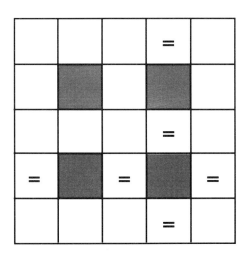

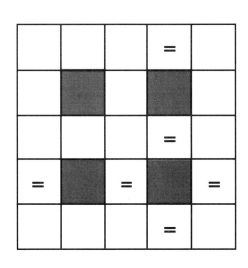

This page may be copied (see page 2) © Collins Educational 1992.

Special paper 5

This page may be copied (see page 2) © Collins Educational 1992.